Hobbs

TANGLEY FARM

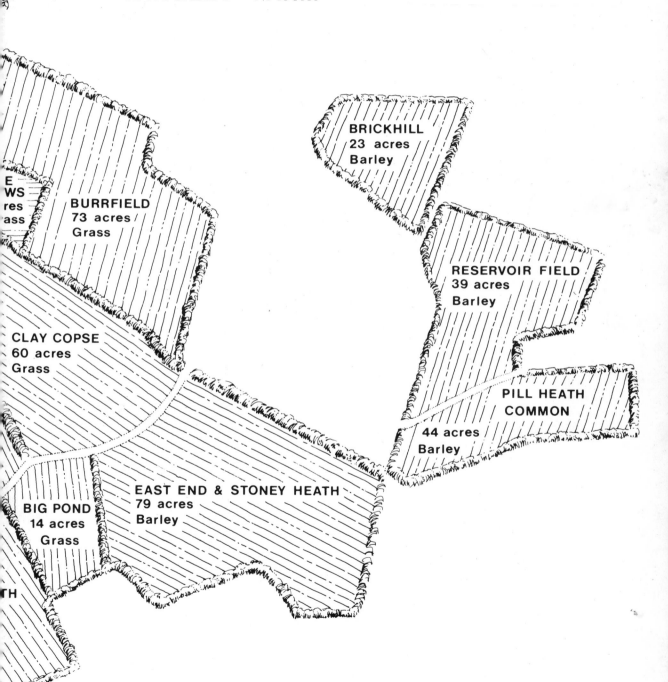

E
WS
res
ass

BURRFIELD
73 acres
Grass

BRICKHILL
23 acres
Barley

RESERVOIR FIELD
39 acres
Barley

CLAY COPSE
60 acres
Grass

PILL HEATH
COMMON

44 acres
Barley

BIG POND
14 acres
Grass

EAST END & STONEY HEATH
79 acres
Barley

TH

A FARMING YEAR

By the same author

On The Smell Of An Oily Rag
Lifting My Nose From The Grindstone

A FARMING YEAR
JOHN CHERRINGTON

Illustrations by Bernard Venables

HODDER AND STOUGHTON
LONDON SYDNEY AUCKLAND TORONTO

British Library Cataloguing in Publication Data

Cherrington, John
  A farming year
  1. Farms – Great Britain
  I. Title
  338.1'0941   HD1925
ISBN 0 340 28209 6

Contents

· Contents ·

Introduction

I was not born into farming, but I chose it as a career because farmers always seemed to me to have an independence from the regimentation of ordinary life, to be able to do as they liked when they liked, and need call no man their master. This suited me. I loathed boarding school and resented authority in any form.

It was an approach based entirely on a profound ignorance of the real facts of farming; of having every operation dependent on the weather, of living at the mercy of irrational market fluctuations quite outside my control, and even more arbitrary government action or lack of action. Even the time I chose was unpropitious. World wide, farming was in decline. Farmers were beginning to leave the land in droves, even in Britain sensible farmers' sons were trying to get into banks.

My father was in fact a banker but when I refused to go to Cambridge, saying I wanted to use the money as my starting capital, he agreed, and after leaving school I spent a while on a farm in Shropshire. Thus fortified I emigrated to New Zealand in 1928 believing in my ignorance that empty land was there for the taking. I soon found out my mistake. Even then New Zealand was closely settled and well farmed, but prices were low and land costs high – a phenomenon which I have never really understood.

After working as a shepherd for a couple of years I found that economic circumstances were steadily worsening and even getting a job was difficult. So I took ship to the Argentine in charge of a flock of sheep and worked there for another two years before returning to England.

While working on the pampas, I had read *Farmer's Glory* by A. G. Street. Still in my view the best farming book ever written, certainly that I have ever read. In my ignorance and arrogance I thought that I could do as well or better than the author in England.

What skills I had picked up as a shepherd or cowhand had little application on the smaller British farms, but I had one great advantage. In both countries where I had worked, economic farming conditions were much worse than in Britain. Those I had worked for were surviving by being able to cut expenditure to the bone and denying themselves almost every luxury. I knew as soon as I came back to England and had a look round that I could do as well as the locals or even better if I followed these precepts. And I was right.

I took the tenancy of my first farm in west Wiltshire on Michaelmas Day, September 29th, 1933. This is the traditional date for the beginning of the

7

farming year. It was a mixed grass and arable farm of 500 acres with a seven-bedroomed farmhouse and four cottages for which I paid 13s.0d an acre or £325 a year. I had just enough capital to pay the ingoing valuations and buy the stock and equipment to run it.

The main source of income was from a herd of seventy cows which were milked in a moveable cowstall or bail which was moved from field to field. This system avoided the need for expensive cowstalls and muck handling, the cows were their own muck spreaders and by this means the pastures were gradually improved. I grew wheat and oats and had a herd of sows as well . . .

I was just about playing myself into the farm when I received notice to quit by September 29th, 1935, as my landlord wanted to sell the farm for family reasons. I found two other farms to rent near Andover in Hampshire only one of which had a farmhouse in which I could live. My move enabled me to double my acreage, and my cow numbers, and because land was almost unsaleable and unlettable at that time I secured further parcels of land when the opportunity arose.

Then I received notice to quit the farm where I was living by September, 1940. This insecurity of tenancy determined me to avoid landlords in the future where I could. I bought, on mortgage, a house in a nearby village and from there built up a large acreage of rented land most of which I eventually bought on long-term fixed-interest mortgages.

I bought my farm at Tangley in 1947 and have lived here ever since, other farms are now owned by my sons, and I have the remnants of a large farming business to myself. This book gives a monthly record of what should be happening on the farm month by month throughout the year. I say 'should' advisedly. No blueprint ever drawn could possibly be followed except in outline within the constraints imposed by the eccentricities of the British climate and animal physiology.

I have chosen to begin the book in October because September 29th, Michaelmas Day, is the traditional date for the beginning of the farming year, a time when rents fall due and when farms change hands. There are good practical reasons too. By the end of September, the cereal harvest should be over with the grain in store, or sold, and the farmer can therefore start afresh with his own preparations for next year's crop.

October

This can be a beast of a month; the decisions about what to plant where should have been made weeks or months ago, but implementation of these decisions is made difficult by the eccentricity of the weather and the shortening days. Two thirds of next year's harvest has to be planted and, for sheep farmers like myself, the bulk of the ewes must go to the ram. It's a time of frustration and short temper for both farmer and men . . .

I have some 900 acres here at Tangley in north Hampshire, including 200 acres rented, of which just under 800 are arable, that is they can be used for cropping. The remainder consists of unploughable areas of downland, and other fields salvaged from woodlands which are suitable for grazing-pasture. The soil-type varies from easy-working loams to clay and flint on the hilltops.

The clay-cap soils on the tops of the hills were once used for brick-making. There are in fact old brick-workings at the summit of the farm and the men who used to work them were still alive when I first came here.

Clay is a difficult soil to cultivate, being impermeable to water and quickly becoming waterlogged. On drying out, it is just as bad, turning brick-hard and refusing to crumble down to make a good mould in which to plant the seed; instead one gets rough lumps in which a tilth is just impossible.

Flints are another difficulty. Where they occur, they are held very firmly by the clay, and for this reason the various pieces of farm machinery with which they come in contact wear out much more rapidly than on easier land. They are also a great drawback with such crops as potatoes and sugar-beet, whose growing tubers cannot push the flints aside as they can in easier soils. Flints have been a problem in these parts for centuries and when labour was plentiful and cheap, hundreds of thousands of tonnes of them were picked off the fields and used for roads and for building houses.

So my land is expensive to cultivate, but it has one other defect which must be mentioned here. Most of the subsoil of the Hampshire hills is pure chalk. Where the chalk is near the surface, the soils are alkaline or sweet. But the clay caps are the very opposite, sour, with the strong probability that unless they have lime in the form of chalk applied to them, crops will not grow.

This was certainly realised in the old days; all over the clay cap on my farm there are the remains of shafts which used to be sunk into the underlying chalk. This was tunnelled out and winched to the surface where it was spread over the fields by hand, wheelbarrow and donkey. Such heavy tonnages were applied in this way, probably during the early nineteenth century, that their benefits have lasted until now.

Every so often one of these old workings subsides and some quite dangerous holes appear in the fields. My tractor-drivers watch out for them. A few years before I came to Tangley, a horse-team disappeared out of sight and was only rescued with difficulty. Today I buy my lime from a quarry some miles away, but I am thinking of opening up a chalk quarry on my own farm because I notice that signs of lime deficiency are becoming more apparent every year.

Cereal crops are in the soil for at least six to ten months and may not be harvested and sold for as much as a year after they have been planted. Meanwhile the arable farmer has no money coming in and has to finance himself. Therefore I am a mixed farmer and don't simply rely on crops for a living. I used to milk cows but then I gave my dairy herd to one of my sons. This immediately caused difficulties with my bank balance; I missed the regular monthly milk cheque which came in without fail the year round so I decided to ease my cash flow by keeping a flock of 1,200 breeding ewes. However, although I farmed quite profitably with arable crops and sheep, my overdraft obstinately refused to decrease so I decided to set up a herd of about 120 sows. Sheep and pigs don't have to be milked twice a day which is a great relief, but I still miss my cows because I began my life as a dairy farmer, and it is through my milking herd that I survived my early years.

In the old days there was a clear demarcation between arable and dairy farmers. The grain-grower was a capitalist and in good times he lived like one and would have very little to do socially with dairy farmers who would spend seven days a week milking. Marriage between the two classes was frowned upon, but past history has shown that in the end it is the dairy farmers who inherit, if not the earth, then at least their rich neighbours' farms. For in times of slump the monthly milk cheque enables the dairy farmer to survive, as it did me.

Arable farming has been characterised by periods of boom and slump since the end of the Napoleonic wars. It took farmers twenty-five years to recover from the post-Waterloo slump, a boom then followed until 1848 when the repeal of the Corn Laws allowed in masses of cheap grain. By 1879 vast areas of arable land in Britain, particularly in East Anglia and the South, went into decline and hosts of farmers left the land.

The leavers were replaced by farmers' sons from the livestock areas of Devon and Cornwall, western Scotland and Wales. Because of their hardier upbringing and because they were prepared to bring cows on to their farms, they survived the bad patches and so were able to enjoy the brief boom created by the first world war.

Prices rose and after the Great War the government of the day promised farmers an Act of Parliament which would ensure reasonable prices in peacetime. In June 1921, the government announced a sudden reversal of policy: farmers were to be left on their own to compete against imports from every country in the world. The worst-hit were the cereal growers. Dairymen and other livestock interests survived, helped by the cheap grain imports which provided foodstuffs for animals, but pure arable farmers had few facilities for suddenly changing to stock; there was often neither water nor fencing on their land and they did not have any spare capital with which to buy flocks and herds.

Arable farmers had also been rather spoilt after seven years of rising prices from 1914 to 1921. Some had initially paid big prices for their land in the expectation of permanently high returns from grain and now that these had been halved, they were in great trouble. Moreover their life-styles had developed to match their substantial incomes.

Some did survive, supported by their carefully saved wartime profits, but most succumbed in spite of extended credit and landlords who remitted rents. In the arable areas of Britain, derelict land was increasingly common and landlords desperate to find tenants. By 1933, when I was looking for a farm, the slump was really on and prices for land and stock were at rock bottom. I should qualify this: arable land was at a discount but good grassland farms were not easily found because grass will grow without cultivation and can be turned into money through milking cows.

When I took over the tenancy of my first farm in west Wiltshire I thought that I would be able to farm it in the way I wanted. I found, though, that for the 150 acres already under the plough, my lease laid down the exact sequence in which these were to be cropped. Penalties were also written into the lease and I should incur these if I declined to do as the landlord ordered. I found that I might have to pay a heavy bill on quitting for having cropped out of rotation: I might even lose the farm altogether.

I was not to allow one white straw or cereal crop to succeed another directly. The landlord's rotation was based on the Norfolk four-course system organised round the building up of fertility for wheat, the most profitable crop. Wheat was to be followed by roots, either turnips or brassica, which would be eaten off by sheep, whose dung would manure the land. Next came spring barley or oats, undersown with clover, from which a hay crop could be taken the following year. The clover would be followed by wheat once more, then the whole process would start again, which meant that the cropping of any specific field could be determined for years ahead.

By the 1930s, the rigidity of these rules was being relaxed in some areas because with farming in the depths of the inter-war depression, landlords could not afford to pick and choose between those who would, or would not, be prepared to carry out their specific rotational ideas. My landlord gave me freedom of cropping except in the last year of my tenancy. That must have been the original Catch 22 because to get the land back into a four-course rotation once you had not been following it would have taken three to four years.

When I took over my new farm, I had to pay for a field of rye which my predecessor had sown as sheep-feed, but I had no sheep then. One of my neighbours offered to send his sheep over to feed off the rye, but being very young, I failed to name a price. After a while, I broached the subject. He exploded. Did I not appreciate, he said, that his sheep deposited dung which would benefit my next crop? Were it not for our friendship, he would have been entitled to charge me for the incidental manuring his sheep had given my land. I said no more, but the experience taught me much about farmers. However I must be lacking in his forcefulness for I have never managed to get one of my neighbours to keep my sheep for nothing, although I have tried.

The theory of modern rotation was imported from the Continent towards the end of the eighteenth century when farmers came to realise that cereals were subject to infection from the residues of the previous crops and that they needed the fertility given by animal manure to increase yield. The principles of rotational farming have been improved since then by the gradual introduction of fertilisers and modified by modern needs to meet the economics of the day, but they are still practised to some extent. Economics come into the question because although there are cures for the diseases which can be passed from

12

crop to crop and although pesticides exist to kill a wide variety of bugs, they cost money. Some of us still believe therefore that rotation means something. So in a compromise with modernity I do still, to some extent, rotate my crops.

Uncle Jack, an adopted relative, used to tell me about a cousin of his who farmed a conventional arable four-course rotation until he took to his bed at the age of thirty, for no very good reason, and never left his room for thirty-five years. During all this time his old head-carter farmed for him most successfully for he knew exactly what should be planted in each field from year to year. Then there was a catastrophe: the carter died, the farmer left his bed, thought up some new fancy ideas and went bankrupt.

The rotation I practise in these days in Hampshire is a far cry from the Norfolk rotation of my early farming days, but it hasn't bankrupted me yet. It is governed by cash returns. Cereals: wheat, barley and oats are saleable, and the first two have prices directly guaranteed by the European Economic Community system. But turnips and clover have very little sale value, even if fed through livestock. By a process of trial and error I have now arrived at a system which gives me a grass break every four to seven years. After a crop of winter barley has been harvested, grass is sown in the late summer and heavily grazed by sheep for the next twelve months, then it is ploughed and sown to wheat.

It is essential that the grass should yield a return to match an average cereal crop and the only way in which I have found this possible is to stock the field with ewes and lambs. The lambs thrive because this grass has not yet become contaminated with the pests which invade older pastures and which can cause lambs serious problems. On this soil, I have found that mixing sheep and cereal crops, alternate husbandry as it is called, keeps my farming reasonably well balanced.

There are of course other break-crops besides grass, but I have not found them profitable. Potatoes are not easy on my flinty soil. Peas and grass seed are of unreliable yield here and there is no nearby factory to process sugar-beet.

Once I have decided on my cropping for the coming year, it is time to prepare the soil and clean it of weeds, for it is no use planting a crop only to have it eventually choked and smothered by alien vegetation. Sadly weeding is not a once-and-for-all operation but has to be carried out several times during the year as different weeds have to be dealt with at different stages in their growth.

The worst to my mind are a number of grass-like weeds which, being of much the same family as the cereal plant, are difficult to eradicate, as they cannot be sprayed out of the crop in the same way as the broad-leaved weeds. These grass weeds have a roughly similar growth-pattern to that of cereals, some of them are perennial, so if they are not killed outright by pre-emergent spraying before the cereal crop is planted, they grow with it, mature with it and shed their seeds just when the cereals are being harvested.

One of the worst is couch-grass or *Agropyron repens*, which spreads below ground level through a system of roots which makes it very difficult to kill. Until a few years ago, the only way to combat this particular weed was a summer

13

fallow. The land would be left bare for a whole summer, and repeatedly moved with a variety of implements. Eventually ploughing, harrowing and working over with a large-tined implement called a cultivator would kill the couch. But this was expensive, requiring the whole summer to make sure of an absolute kill; any thought of growing a crop in that particular field that year had to be forgotten because by the time the couch was dead, the time for planting was over.

Some farmers used to try to hurry the process by raking the couch into heaps and burning it. W. H. Hudson in *A Shepherd's Life*, talks nostalgically of 'the smell of the couch fires'. Before the war I used sometimes to indulge in this practice, hauling great mounds of couch into pyres and setting them alight. The trouble was that the burning seldom killed all the couch, and in damp weather hardly any of it, so the battle seemed never-ending, particularly on very light chalkland such as the Wiltshire downs, where the couch-rhizomes spread rapidly below ground. The lighter the soil, the easier their passage, and the underground rhizome system of each couch-grass plant can advance by as much as a metre a year.

Now science has come to the rescue with a chemical which will kill off couch-grass quite successfully and I am gradually ridding my land of this weed, although I am still having trouble in Great Heath field. But as sure as night follows day, something else will arise to take couch's place. Meanwhile the new chemical is difficult to use for, to be fully effective, it has to be applied when the weed is growing most vigorously. At this stage the actual crop in the infested field is still standing. A technique has therefore to be devised whereby the spraying of the chemical causes minimum damage to the unharvested crop, since, unless an aeroplane is used, the sprayer has to be towed across the field.

A few years ago it would have been considered the height of folly to drive a tractor through a standing crop but now it happens all the time. Many will have seen the wheel-marks or tramlines running through growing crops these days, where the drill seems to have missed. These are deliberately set out so that the spraying machinery can move up and down the field without doing too much damage. Some farmers have their drill or planting-machines especially set out for the job, never planting these rows at all. Others rely on following, throughout the season, the tracks made by the machine at the first application. I confess that on my own farm, I take the latter course. There is always a hope that I shall not have to spray anything and so save a good deal of money. If I leave tramlines however there is always a temptation to use them.

Tramlining stemmed from the Continent. Professor Laloux of Belgium was the first to persuade farmers that if they monitored the progress of cereal crops throughout the growing season, outbreaks of disease could be corrected immediately by the right quantity of chemical or fertiliser. This was absolutely revolutionary. For the first forty years of my farming life all I did was to plant the seed with the right amount of basic fertiliser, apply a small amount of nitrogenous fertiliser in the spring to give the crop a boost, perhaps also a weed-killer, then shut the gate until harvest. But no longer. Today, the mark of a progressive farmer is that his knees are muddied. Why? Because he spends most of his time on them, magnifying-glass in hand, studying the development of his crop. Few spores or aphids now escape his eagle eye. I found that it took a great deal of resolution to resist the example of progressive, muddy-kneed neighbours, who were obviously doing all they could to safeguard their future harvests, so I followed suit.

By early in the month, I hope, I shall have sprayed my land clear of most of the weeds, so that I can now set about preparing the soil to receive the seed. This means ploughing, as it is the only way to make my soil friable enough for the seed-drill to pass through and for the soil itself to be capable of forming a good bed in which the seed can set out its roots and grow. If the soil is harsh and chiselly, the seed will not germinate, or will only do so irregularly.

Ploughing is a slow and expensive job and means that the turn-furrows move several hundred tonnes of soil on every acre, but it breaks up the ground, buries weeds and helps with the drainage. There are those today who believe in minimal cultivation, in doing the least possible in the way of earth-moving; these farmers drill the seed straight into the soil with a special machine. But when we tried this at Tangley, it was not a success. My clay soil is difficult to penetrate and where we did manage to plant, we were later frustrated by a weed called sterile or barren brome-grass.

Why such a pest should be called sterile I cannot say. It lives in the hedgerows and the seed, a kind of tiny oat, invades the adjoining crop where it ripens and drops before harvest. On my land, after two years of minimal cultivation, sterile brome was taking over. Chemical treatment does kill this weed but is far from being one hundred per cent effective. Fortunately someone found that the seeds of brome-grass cannot germinate if buried six inches deep, so a simple solution was to plough every vulnerable field.

The pros and cons to be considered over the relative merits of autumn and spring sowing are legion. Certainly autumn-sown cereals are thought to yield rather better than those sown in the spring. These over-wintering varieties are specially bred for the job and include in their make-up a factor that demands exposure to low temperature to make them perform at their best. That is the plus side, but it is also becoming clear that autumn sowing has its disadvantages, making it easier for disease to attack the growing crops simply because they are longer in the ground.

In a mild British winter there is often a great deal of growth which encourages the spread of disease and fungal infections. But the generally damp state of the ground makes it very difficult to apply remedies. In addition the very speed necessary to complete autumn sowing before the advent of bad weather makes it impossible entirely to destroy all the previous crop residues which can pass on infections. But by February most of such trash should have been ploughed under, and, it is hoped, will no longer be a source of disease.

In Europe where most grain is autumn-sown, the Continental climate is much colder than that of Britain and in general there is a period of frost or nil growth for several months. This not only stops the crops growing, but prevents disease from developing.

Whatever the potential problems in Britain, I am completely convinced that for the highest yields wheat must be autumn-sown, as few varieties of spring-sown wheat have been very successful up to now. Barley is another matter. Until ten years ago the only reliable barleys were the spring-sown varieties. But then Continental winter barleys became available which in good conditions far out-yielded the spring ones and like many farmers I took them up in a big way.

Apart from yield, winter barley has a further advantage; it comes to harvest at least a month before wheat and spring barley. This means that I can get a proportion of my harvest out of the way in July and start to prepare the ground for grass-seed sowing before the rest of the harvest is ready. It also means that I can spread my harvest load. An autumn-sown crop also eases my spring sowing.

Unfortunately problems have arisen: winter-barley varieties are not only particularly vulnerable to diseases which don't affect the spring-sown ones, they also need more fertilising, so it now looks as though extra costs outweigh the benefits of increased yields and earlier harvest.

A couple of years ago when the autumn-sowing craze was at its height I tried to get all my 600 acres of cereals in then – and almost succeeded. Since that time however, I have become increasingly relaxed with only two-thirds autumn-sown now and probably less in the future. I am leaning towards reducing the winter-barley proportion of this and might well eventually return entirely to the spring-sown varieties.

I save about half the seed I plant from my own harvest and buy the balance

through the trade which ensures that I have a supply of good-quality seed on the farm. Plant breeders have been steadily improving the quality and particularly the yields of cereals over the last thirty years and average yields have doubled in that time. I would say that at least half this improvement comes from breeding, and the balance from new ideas in fertilising and disease control.

As you will appreciate, the autumn stresses on an arable farmer are considerable, for the time between the end of the main harvest and the sowing season is short and into this period must be crammed weed-killing, ploughing, drilling and seeding. If the weather is hot, the land may be too hard and dry to plough; if the rain has been heavy, the earth may be too sticky and glutinous to work. There is an old saying that barley should be sown in dust and wheat in mud but I resist the urge to hustle and plant immediately after the harvest. Farmers are very competitive people and it is hard to stand by whilst one's neighbours plant early, nevertheless I like to take a steady pace. When winter barley was first introduced the practice was to sow very early indeed so that the plant was really strong and thick by November, but in general this forced growth resulted in quite bad attacks of mildew and other diseases. The plant usually survived as the frosts took off the diseased leaves, but it seemed to some of us that the best way to avoid mildew was to plant a little later, so I aim to start sowing my barley during the first week in October and to finish by the middle of the month.

Both winter barley and winter wheat need to be exposed to a degree of cold sufficient to stop all growth for a little, after which they will grow much better when the warm weather finally does arrive. The main advantage of early sowing is that as the land gets progressively wetter through the autumn, it becomes more difficult to work, otherwise, as far as I am concerned, winter wheat can be sown at any time until just before Christmas. The wheat plant has an enormous capacity for recovery once growth starts in the spring; as long as the newly-sown seeds have germinated and are looking vigorous before the onset of frosts in December, I am quite happy. When I used to grow potatoes and sugar-beet, I was often very late planting wheat after harvesting them and I don't remember that results showed a lower yield.

October is not only a very important month on the land, but it is also a very busy one in the stockman's calendar. I have a flock of 1,200 ewes on my farm, and reckon to mate the bulk of my flock in this month. For the last twenty years I have been buying in from Cumbria a Greyface or Mule ewe lamb, a cross between a Blue-Faced Leicester ram and a Swaledale ewe. I then cross this lamb when it is old enough with a Suffolk ram. As my ewes are crossbred from the mountain breeds, they take the ram most naturally in October so that they lamb late in March to avoid bad weather. This has been bred into them by centuries of natural selection; only those born late survived, and these in turn had the characteristic of late lambing, which of course meant late mating. Some of the lowland breeds will take the ram earlier, but in general these do not have as many lambs as those mated later.

There are various means of synchronising oestrus, so that lambing can be

concentrated into a very short time, but the thought of having to lamb 1,200 ewes in less than a week, and the labour that would be needed to deal with them, fills me with horror. Such mass lambing might also coincide with some appalling weather conditions, so I try to organise the lambing in three stages. A lamb takes about five calendar months to gestate so a small number are mated after mid-September to lamb in late February; these will be in good condition for sale early in the summer. The bulk of the flock are mated from October 7th onwards and the young ewes, two-tooths as we call them, are mated from October 18th. These last have never lambed before and we farm them as a separate flock through most of the winter.

As the time of mating is said to be controlled by light, various attempts have been made to alter mating-times by artificially stimulating the decreasing light of autumn, for instance by shutting the ewes in a barn, but so far as I know, this has never been really successful.

But successful lambing is not just a matter of timing. The aim is to have as many lambs as possible and for this the ewes have to be in the peak of condition at mating. This is called flushing. Farmers used to go to great lengths to provide lush feed for their ewes in late summer as the theory was that this caused them to ovulate freely and so produce two, or even three, lambs. Flushing does not just mean that the ewes should be fat. What matters is that they should be on a rising plane of condition after the stresses of rearing their last lot of lambs. This is not simply a matter of body weight. I have had some very disappointing results with ewes mated when really fat and concluded that the reason was that their metabolism had spent itself reaching their top weight and was now static, with the urge to growth in reverse, as it were. Ovulation suffered in consequence.

The practice at Tangley is to keep the ewes on a fairly tight margin until the end of August and then give them good feed for the next six weeks. This is often more easily said than done because the climate is infinitely variable but, generally speaking, we have a dampish September, the grass grows, and so the plan works.

I have two rams for every hundred ewes. I turn my twenty-five Suffolk rams out with the ewes, with their bellies coloured with a mixture of oil and red or blue ochre which comes off on the backs of the ewes they have covered. From this it is possible to know how the mating process is going and, more particularly, when the marked ewes are going to lamb. About 80 per cent of the ewes take the ram at the first mating so will be likely to lamb five months later. The ewes' oestrus cycle is seventeen days, so in general the colour is changed every seventeen days, but in a big flock it might be changed weekly so that after mating the ewes can be separated into different flocks and their management suited to the period of their pregnancy.

I like to time it so that the bulk of the ewes, with their lambs at foot, will be ready to meet the increased grass growth which normally starts in mid-March, but I always have a few who trickle into late March or early April.

I am very attached to my sheep in spite of their economic drawbacks. Take depreciation. A ewe at the time of writing costs sixty pounds, and will on average have about one and a half lambs once a year. But if she makes a mess of her lambing, ending up with none, she is worth perhaps twenty-five pounds. My pigs, on the other hand, will produce at any time of the year, independent of the seasons. They are much more prolific, with sixteen to twenty pigs a year, from a properly managed sow in two farrowings, and these will be saleable from eight weeks to six months old. If my sow is barren, she can still be sold for anything up to a hundred pounds for making sausages. This means that there is little or no depreciation on a pig herd, but there is on a flock of sheep, and to a certain extent on dairy cows.

My 120 sows produce each year just under 2,000 pigs, which are sold for the fresh-meat trade as pork. Once a week the lorry comes to take thirty-five to forty pigs off the farm and a cheque for their value turns up the following week. This is not all profit of course; my pigs eat barley grown on the farm and I have to buy proteins for them as well. But turnover is very quick, my porkers being ready for sale some twenty weeks after they are born. Compare this with the income from a flock of ewes, where the sale of lambs and wool might with luck reach fifty pounds per head and where payment will be concentrated in about three summer months; then there is grain, which takes at least a year, if not more, to grow and to sell. Mixed farming has many advantages. But there is no way that sheep can be made to pay modern land-costs, only old-established farmers such as myself can afford them. Two of my sons have already ousted their flocks.

November

An old farmer told me that in 1895 it began to freeze early in the month, and that by the 10th ploughing was impossible and so it remained until the following April. On the other hand, there is a saying that if the ice bears a duck in November, it will not do so again through the winter. There is yet another old saw to the effect that after the first of November, it either rains or freezes every night. There is something in this. A clear sky will usually bring frost and a cloudy one rain, or the threat of it.

If there is not too much frost I'll be planting my winter wheat. Elsewhere potatoes and particularly sugar-beet are being harvested. There is some grass growth as long as there are few frosts but persistent frost at this time can wipe out grass, and if it is really severe prevent land-work altogether. In that case I shall set about selling some of the wheat and barley which is stored in my silos.

In the old days November used to be the ideal month for spreading dung. About half the fields would have still been in stubble awaiting the plough but that was before the days of stubble hygiene. The theory today is that the residue of the last crop carries disease so the quicker everything combustible is burnt off, the better. As soon as the harvest is finished every weed and growing plant is attacked by fire, chemicals and cultivation at speed. As a result the stubble field has all but disappeared in modern farming. Instead the November landscape shows either bare soil or the green of the newly-growing wheat and barley. It is possible of course to spread dung on bare soil but if it has been cultivated at all, it will be soft, and the heavy machinery used in these days will make an awful mess if it is wet. Dung is a valuable plant-food but finding somewhere to spread it is a never-ending problem. Not sheep dung, for sheep drop it where they graze, but cow and pig dung. The great heaps of pig dung I collect are an infernal nuisance for I cannot spread them on my grass pastures as they contain a high proportion of potash, and potash can induce a disease among ewes which kills them. My only hope is to leave a grass field due to be ploughed near my pig units and spread as much dung on it as I can, but it's not easy to organise this. If only someone would come and buy, or even steal, my pig dung, how happy I would be. As it is, I have to keep great seeping heaps of it until summer, when, with luck, I may get a chance to spread it quickly on the arable fields immediately after they've been burnt.

I am a firm believer in the use of the plough and all my land which is not in crop, being sown this month or down to pasture, should now be turned over and left for the winter. I like to get the job finished in November in case there are early frosts in December which will stop the ploughs completely. The effect of frost on land which is ploughed is very beneficial; it makes even the most unpromising of clay soils break down into a good tilth once the land begins to dry out again in the early spring.

Modern ploughing does not leave the land in the symmetrical furrows that used to be the rule. That is the standard of the ploughing-match. The farmer wants a system which is fast and leaves the land well roughed-up to take the weather; if all the stubble and other trash has been disposed of meticulous workmanship is not needed. The modern plough with fourteen to sixteen inch furrows is designed for this job. It throws the soil right over, without turning it.

Traditional ploughing nowadays is reserved for turning grassland into arable where it is essential to bury every last scrap of turf so that it cannot grow again. This is a slow job. It stands to reason that a plough travelling fast over the field is in much more danger of jumping out of its furrow if it hits a stone than one pulled at a steady pace.

22

I was never much of a ploughman myself, in fact the last time I did any was in New Zealand with horses. There was great satisfaction in walking behind a team, seeing the furrow turn over and hearing the hiss of the share passing through the soil. But all the romance has disappeared. Now you just hear the roar of the engine; the furrows unfurl directly behind the tractor so the operator has to crane his neck round to see just how his work is shaping. Speed is king, and the man who used to plough an acre in a long day with horses, walking twenty miles in the process, can cover fifteen to twenty acres with one of the big new tractors.

But whatever my resources in men and machines, I am still very much at the mercy of the weather. My sowing can be prevented by a long drought after harvest or by endless rain which makes the earth sticky and prevents the drill-coulters passing through. Working the land when wet also tends to smarm it down: sometimes the seeds won't penetrate the top soil or the water will lie there in great pools. I have to work with the weather and not against it.

By November, grass is already getting short; it lacks the nutritional value of that in spring although it still looks green and fresh. Sheep will live well on it but not cattle, least of all milking cows. A cow may weigh 1,000 lbs and needs to eat 100 lbs of grass a day with a mouth which is no more than two and a half inches wide. Whereas a sheep with a body weighing some 100 lbs will eat about 10 lbs of grass a day with a mouth whose cutting teeth are about an inch wide. So a cow needs grass which is much longer than that which would satisfy a sheep in order to secure the same proportionate intake of food, since they both have fixed periods for feeding and for chewing the cud which limits grazing-time. A sheep will do very well therefore on grass which at this time of year is no more than an inch or two long. Moreover I do not want to push the ewes too hard in the next month or so for I have already brought them to peak condition for mating. Although they are in lamb, the embryos are very small and not yet making demands. This is the time to let the ewes settle quietly on to a plateau of nutrition.

When I had a milking herd of nearly 200 cows, November would have seen them at peak milking yield for I would have tried to get most of them to calve in early October. This may seem like going against nature in a big way because in the wild most grazing animals give birth in the spring so that they can take advantage of the better feed available. But the move towards October calving was created by the need to maintain a steady flow of milk for people to drink throughout the year. Spring-calving cows are usually dry before the end of November so the Milk Boards always gave a higher price to encourage winter milk. It was also found that the autumn-calving cows gave much higher lactation yields than did spring calvers, so that now, even if EEC membership has caused milk prices to be level through most of the year, farmers still try in the main to have the bulk of their cows calving in the autumn, although not all cows conceive at the first mating so there is always some slippage towards spring calving.

A cow is in oestrus every three weeks so I would give each animal three services over a period of six weeks if she failed to conceive the first time. The gestation period is nine months, so, to achieve autumn calves, I would have had to see that my cows were mated from mid-December on. Successful conception was more likely if they were well fed and in peak condition. These cows would then be turned out to grass at the end of March, when the grass was good, which would enable them to carry on giving excellent yields of milk until the end of July. They would then be dried off and rested before calving in October. The minority of farmers who calve their herds in the spring provide the bulk of the milk between July and October.

All milk sales in Britain are controlled by the Milk Marketing Boards which are the sole buyers and wholesalers of milk from the farm gate. They enforce quality standards by the use of premiums and have, by and large, satisfied both farmers and buyers, although whether the consumer has been satisfied has not been placed on record. Before the Boards' inception in 1933 farmers were on their own when they sold, and the buyers could do as they liked, and they did.

I was a farm manager in Shropshire then, and had some 300 cows in my charge. The milk was collected every day by the buyer's lorry, which left the churns for the next day's output. At the peak of summer production, the lorry would cut down the number of churns, with the result that we had nowhere to put all the milk produced. We used all sorts of baths, tubs and other containers, and we also built up a secret store of churns, during the period of low production, by pinching one or two off the lorry while the driver was getting a cup of tea. All the buyers played mean tricks in those days and there was little to choose between them.

Milk Marketing Boards were meant to put an end to such sharp practices as they arranged for all the milk produced in England and Wales to be pooled on a regional basis, but this in itself led to some interesting anomalies, for the pool price varied from region to region. I found that when I moved from the farm I rented in Wiltshire to Tangley in Hampshire, I was able to increase the earnings of a seventy-cow dairy herd by one penny a gallon, or 15 per cent.

My dairy-farming methods in those days of deep depression were very different from the sophisticated systems now in use. I could not afford to build expensive sheds in which to winter my cows so I kept them out in the fields instead. I milked them out in the fields, too, from cheap moveable open-air sheds, or bails as they were called, which I dragged from field to field every few days. The cows were largely shorthorns of a variety of brown colours, a breed seldom seen now. Land was cheap so it didn't greatly matter if the cows trod out the pastures during the winter weather. Production and productivity were very low but the system paid and the effects of each cow spreading its own dung gradually improved my pastures.

Many farmers thought that my herd would suffer in bad weather, for keeping cows out in fields all winter was a novelty, but I found that they would stand any amount of bad weather without harm if well fed. Their hooves did tend to poach and trample low-lying grassland but they did well on drier chalk pastures. Only very wet land would have been so muddied that grass would not have grown again in the spring. But forty years ago farming was extensive and could sacrifice a few fields to winter treading. Now costs are so high that all land must produce to the maximum so very few herds are outwintered.

Over the years I progressed to stationary milking-plants and then back to moveable ones, and the cows changed too, from Shorthorns to Ayrshires, and then finally to the Black and White Friesians from Holland, which make up most of the dairy herd of Britain today. By the time I finished keeping cows my original yields had more than doubled and the techniques of feeding and pasture management had become very intensive indeed.

If November planting and ploughing is up to schedule and I have a spare moment, now is the time to think about selling some of the wheat and barley I have stored up in silos on the farm. On-farm storage is peculiar to England and is a survival from the days before the combine-harvester was invented. Then standing crops were cut with a binder into sheaves which were stooked to dry in the fields, they were then carted off and built into ricks which were thatched against the rain. These ricks were threshed out when the farmer had men to spare and was in need of cash. Binding, stooking, carting, ricking, threshing meant much double handling, the actual job of threshing was also labour-intensive and much grain was lost to the depredations of birds and rats. The whole system was time-consuming and costly. Many farmers in need of ready cash were forced to sell their grain immediately after harvest when prices were traditionally low.

When combine-harvesters came in, in the early 1940s, in common with most of my neighbours, I put in sufficient storage to hold all the grain I could grow, so that I could sell it when I thought prices were at their best. At the same time I also installed a drier; these had not been needed before because a stack acted as a kind of drier for, unlike a hayrick, air could pass through the dry straw which prevented overheating. Heating would have ruined the grain. Air cannot circulate naturally in a full silo so it is essential to dry the grain first by blowing hot air through it until it reaches a moisture-content of less than 14 per cent in order that it will keep without going mouldy. My yields have trebled in the last forty years and are still pushing upwards, so I am continually extending my storage capacity.

Getting a good price for grain is still a bargaining matter, as it has been through the ages, but there are safety-nets based on Common Market guarantees which put a bottom in the market. But I certainly don't rely on basic prices; I want to get as much as I can above them.

I try to sell some of my barley for malting. Malting quality is a very subjective element entirely dependent on market supply. If there are ample quantities of good malting barley around, the premiums for this over the price paid for feed-barley are derisory. If however there should be a shortage of suitable grain, top prices are paid for almost anything.

There are good malting varieties available but they suffer from two defects: they do not yield very well, and their quality can be very variable. When I started farming the intrinsic worth of malting barley was judged entirely by eye. The grains were assessed on their size and shape, and were cut to see if they were white and floury, good; or hard and flinty, bad. The thickness of their skins was also a very telling point, to say nothing of their colour. A nice soft gold was supposed to be just right for making pale ale.

Then in the 60s the scientists took over. The new generation of buyers looked cursorily at the samples, then took them home to test the quantity of nitrogen they contained. The lower the nitrogen, the higher the quality for the new mechanised malting systems. A great friend of mine was one of the first of these buyers. He is now the head of a very big firm and probably the biggest barley-buyer in Britain. He has never owned, or even used, a barley-cutter to see what the inside of the grain looks like.

The malting-barley trade used to be an art, conducted by farmers and traders in corn markets up and down the country. Now it's simply a matter of posting off a sample to a number of dealers who will put it on test and then talk about prices. Even then the loads are tested on delivery, and if they fail, can be returned at the farmer's expense.

The maltsters, who are always trying to persuade us to grow malting varieties, will never put up money in advance to back their warm words in favour of this or that variety. This is because the nitrogen factor is very unreliable being dependent on soil and weather conditions outside a farmer's control.

So the varieties I grow are chosen for yield, and if by any chance a maltster wants to buy them he has to outbid the animal-feed industry or my own pigs. I find though that most years I can sell some barley for malting at a small premium.

Having my own storage does give me an independence in the market but it gives no certain guarantee of profit. Driers and silos cost a lot of money to build and maintain. Financing stocks of grain costs money too. At the moment my bank overdraft is costing me 17½ per cent. So a tonne of grain worth £100 at harvest would cost me £17.50 in interest alone to keep for a year, or £1.45 a month.

The price of wheat and barley is supported by an EEC system which gives a monthly increase in the support price equivalent to £1.39 per tonne. So I am losing steadily on interest charges at present. But that is only the beginning of the story. At harvest I can sell the grain with a moisture content of 16 per cent. But for safe storage the moisture content has to be below 14.5 per cent which means higher drying costs and less to sell. Then even on the best farms there are a few rats, mice, birds and other vermin which take their toll.

Very, very occasionally a shortage develops on the market which means that grain storage pays. In general though storing grain on the farm is a mug's game which I do as little of as I can. I try to empty my stores of all but the barley needed for my pigs by the end of December.

The same sort of problems occur over selling wheat. Only a small proportion of English-grown wheat is used by our own millers to make bread flour for us, because the English like a loaf which is mechanically made and which has a shelf-life of several days. To produce, this supermarket type of loaf requires a high percentage of American and Canadian wheat which is much higher in protein than that generally grown in Europe. As a result, at least half of the English wheat crop is sold for animal feedstuffs either in Britain or overseas. The French avoid importing by using their own lower-protein wheats but bake two or three times a day so that the bread is always fresh.

Some high-protein wheats could be grown here but because of climatic conditions their yields are low and, as with the maltsters, millers won't pay premiums unless forced to by market conditions. So farmers grow for yield, and plant-breeders have encouraged this, by producing varieties of very high yield-potential, but low milling-value. There seems to be a direct link between yield and quality with wheat as with barley.

European wheat production has been increasing steadily as a result of the Common Market support system and as the supply for human food far exceeds demand so the surplus has to be made into animal food or exported. EEC subsidies guarantee farmers that if they export their grain they will get 30 per cent to 40 per cent more than the world market price. This has made it more profitable to import cheap grain substitutes, like tapioca, from outside the Community for animal feedstuffs than to feed European grain to our own animals. Tapioca is made from the root of the manioc or cassava plant and is the main staff of human life in the tropics. When the EEC was formed the Dutch and the Germans foresaw that under the EEC system cereals would be very dear, so they set up plants in Thailand and elsewhere to process manioc and organised shipping-lines to bring it to Europe at a discount. I would buy it myself to feed my pigs but I haven't the necessary special machinery in my mill to handle it.

As a result of subsidies, specialist grain-farming has been encouraged within the EEC at the expense of mixed farming and this has already changed European farming patterns. There are very few livestock in the arable-farming areas of northern France or north Germany. The same trend is developing here. I still cling to my livestock, but this is because I have always taken a great interest in them and I like looking after animals. But there is no doubt that I shall soon be in the minority. Moreover animals raise problems; they need constant attention and getting rid of pig dung and cow slurry is now awkward, as I have mentioned.

November is a most important month for my sheep, not on my own farm but several hundred miles further north on the high fells of the Pennines where my ewes are bred. The various mountain breeds, Welsh, Cheviot, Scottish Black-face and Swaledale, form the basic stock for the hybrid sheep which are farmed in the lowlands, for they pass their general toughness and resistance to disease on to their offspring. As I have already explained, I farm a Greyface or

Mule which is the progeny of a Swaledale, which has horns, a black face and long, almost hairy wool. You can see them in thousands along the moorland roads. They are very hardy but because of the harshness of their surroundings in their home territory, they are not very productive.

For the first four years of their breeding lives they are put to Swaledale rams, but in their last year or so on the hills, they are mated with a Blue Faced Leicester. A Blue Faced ram is three or four times the size of a Swaledale, with ridiculously long legs and an enormous Roman nose. It has been developed specifically for mating with the Swaledale and is, by comparison, a very soft sheep, which could not live in the sort of country in which a Swaledale will thrive. It is only put on to the hills for a very short time to mate.

Yet the first cross of this mating is a quite remarkable lamb combining in some degree the sturdy traits of the Swaledales with the growth-rate and milking ability of the Blue Faced Leicester. I buy some 300 of these ewe lambs every autumn to put into my flock and the numbers available are entirely dependent on the conditions ruling during November when the Swaledale ewes are mated. The timing is important for the hill ewes like to lamb in April.

The upland where the Swaledales roam is open moor, for fencing-in land of such low productivity would be expensive and uneconomic. If erected, fences would soon deteriorate in the high rainfall and sharp frosts, moreover they would interfere with the profitable sporting rights, with deer-stalking and grouse-shooting, and no doubt the environmentalists would complain too. Only a few of the ewes are mated in small fields near the farmsteads where the rams can find them; the rest of the rams have to roam the hills in search of their mates. This you would think should be an easy job, after all sex is the most compelling drive in life. But to a ram which has been brought up and kept in luxury on a lowland farm, the open moor is sheer hell. Rather than chase an illusory ewe over the mountains, he would greatly prefer to be back at the farm gate waiting for a bucket of feed or a pitch of hay. Instead he is coloured bright red, so that he can be spotted a long way off, and encouraged by shepherds and sheep-dogs to join with odd flocks of sheep without a ram. A ewe is only in oestrus for a short time so it is essential that a ram is around every day during this period.

Once when I was very much younger, I set out with a shepherd, a man of about twice my age, across some not very high hills, walking sixteen miles or more in pouring rain and occasional fog. He kept to the ridges and worked the sheep with his dog, bringing them in and down and seeing that each small group met with a ram. It was very hard work and I kept on wondering why they did not fence the hills in, as they do in New Zealand, so that the stock could be controlled, but it doesn't ever seem to have appeared worth while to those who farm the moorland areas of Scotland, Wales and England.

When a hill-farm changes hands, the incomer has to buy the sheep native to the farm at valuation. It would be useless to bring fresh sheep in, because of the certainty of losing them. Although the majority of sheep do seem to stay roughly within certain vague limits, simply because that is the area which they know best and in which they were born and bred, the overlap from farm to farm is considerable. As a result there is little incentive to improve the grazing for if the improver's own sheep benefited, then so would those of everyone else for they would soon be drawn in by the better grass. In many areas, much of the hill acreage is held in common and the last people to come to any sort of mutual agreement are commoners.

   I used to buy hill sheep from Wales; these had a very highly developed homing instinct and were difficult to contain at Tangley. On one occasion a load was being taken off a lorry when two young ewes jumped out and set off in a north-westerly direction. The last I heard of them was a police report that they had been seen approaching Swindon twenty-five miles away. I imagine they got home.

December

There is a saying that a green Christmas fills the churchyard, meaning that a period of mild weather fosters diseases which might otherwise be killed off by a spell of frost or snow. There is no medical evidence for this, indeed my doctor told me once that the greener the Christmas the less he had to do.

As a farmer I agree with him. A green December means there is still some grazing to keep the sheep interested, and extra time to clear up any ploughing or other landwork that we have not been able to finish. I have sown wheat in December, but there is a convention, founded on nothing but tradition, that one should not sow wheat after December 12th. Any remaining acreage should be left until the New Year. So this is usually a peaceful period, a time to meet friends out shooting and at fatstock shows such as Smithfield.

There is no real evidence that later sowing restricts yields to any extent. The wheat plant throws out a number of seed-bearing side shoots when growth restarts in the spring, which is called tillering, and this process will begin as early as January in a mild winter. But later-sown crops do not tiller very well so I usually increase the amount of seed planted per acre – the seed rate – as the autumn goes on. I start with about one hundredweight of seed to the acre in October, increase this to one and a half hundredweight in December and add still more in February, which is the last safe time for sowing winter wheat. I do this because it is best to be on the safe side, although I've no proof that the amount of seed planted per acre has any real effect on the final yield. The wheat plant is capable of considerable compensatory growth, and where the density is low, the ears are often much bigger than where it is high.

Heavier seeding is particularly common on farms in north Germany. In Schleswig-Holstein for instance, seed rates are about double ours and farmers spend a great deal of time counting the number of plants to the square metre, making themselves miserable if the answers don't come up to expectation. But they may need to increase their seed rate because, as I have noticed when visiting those parts, their wheat does not tiller in the way mine does, either because the north-German winter is much longer than ours, with little growth in the middle or even at the end of April, or because their varieties of wheat don't tiller as well as they should, even though they seem to yield quite well.

Professor Laloux of Belgium's seed rates are even lower than ours; as he is really the guru of modern European wheat growing, I asked him why he did not follow the German practice. He told me that he had been a prisoner in a forced-labour camp in Germany during the war, and whilst there he had noticed that the Germans always applied double the resources of everyone else to get any job done.

I always think that the shortest day, December 21st, is the nadir of the farming year. Then after Christmas there is a little light at the end of the tunnel of winter, for at last, every day is slightly longer and the sun is gradually getting stronger although the weather in the next few months can be cruel. What I really hate is snow.

My experience is that a real snowfall before the end of the month will make for a very difficult winter. It always falls at the most inconvenient times. My daughter chose to get married on December 29th and, being a home-loving girl, she wanted to have a marquee outside the house. On her wedding day, the route from the church to the marquee was frozen snow six inches deep. We warmed the marquee with one of those hot-air blowing machines which fortunately drowned all the speeches which were, understandably, short. It was snowing hard all the time and we only just got the bride and bridegroom away before all the roads were blocked. The weather had not kept my farming guests away however and something like a bottle of champagne per head disappeared. During the night, the marquee filled with snow and there it remained until the middle of March when a thaw suddenly set in. As the snow melted, the champagne corks and other debris slowly surfaced. The moral is, that if your daughter insists on being married, only co-operate in a June wedding.

I had at that time about a hundred cows wintering in the fields and being milked on an outdoor bail. The cowman had a rough time of it until the snow stopped and he was able to dig the bail out. Getting the milk away was also a problem as most of the roads were blocked, but luckily I had a cross-country lorry, which took the milk to town, and more importantly, brought the empty churns back. Cows are very adaptable creatures and as long as they are well fed, will milk quite well under almost any circumstances. The conditions which will really put the milk-yield back are a combination of high winds and driving rain or snow. Incidentally, filthy weather will also affect cows just as badly when they are lying in open sheds or yards.

My 1,200 ewes don't care much for snow either and have to be given extra feed until the snow melts. One year the first snow fell early in November burying the grass deep. Then I had a stroke of luck. A number of my neighbours had come to a Boxing Day shoot and during lunch one of them told me that as the early snow had melted he did not think he would be able to sell the hundred tonnes of hay he had available. I had a sudden hunch, much better than a computer print-out, that we were in for a really bad winter, so I asked his price and bought the hay then and there. By the time spring came, hay was selling for four times the money, but like most farmers, he stuck to the deal.

Although that particular Boxing Day shoot stood me in good stead, I am not much of a shooting man, particularly at high-driven pheasants. I would much sooner go out with a dog and a friend and try to walk up a few birds but nowadays prosperity has made farmers much more formal in their shooting habits. Back in the 30s when most of us were tenants, the landlord either kept the shoot in hand or let it; in either case the owners did not much care for tenant farmers whom they suspected were knocking off pheasants on the sly. They were quite right too. But then as a tenant, I did not see why I should feed someone else's pheasants through the year but not be allowed to enjoy their consumption. I did bag the occasional one but was careful not to shoot at a pheasant over the top of a hedge for obvious reasons, so I never really learnt to shoot a high bird.

Tenant farmers were allowed to shoot rabbits, in fact they had a right to under the Ground Game Act. I became quite a good rabbit shot as there were literally thousands about; I could even boast of usually being able to kill eleven with every dozen cartridges. There are few rabbits now and the Boxing Day shoot which I generally join is more a social walk around than a slaughter.

I don't mourn the departure of the rabbit, nor the manner of its going, although many non-farmers do as the symptoms of myxomatosis are distasteful to many people. The rabbits' swollen heads and eyes and general comatose condition are indeed unpleasant to look at, but I have always thought it to be a much more merciful end than shooting, traps or gassing. Rabbits were moreover the cause of much economic loss of cash and food, which was not recouped by the sale of their flesh or skins.

Myxomatosis is a virus endemic to South America, where it is comparatively benign. European rabbits however appear to have little resistance to the virus which is carried by the rabbit flea *Spillopsyllus cuniculi*. The virus was introduced into Australia with very considerable success, then a French scientist, Dr Armand Delille, decided to rid himself of a plague of rabbits on his estate by infecting them with the virus. From there myxomatosis escaped and spread over France, crossing the Channel into Sussex and Kent in 1953.

The Ministry of Agriculture tried to stop the spread of the disease for some reason, and fenced-in some woods where it had broken out. But to no avail. The virus spread across England decimating rabbits extremely quickly. This could not have come at a better time for farmers for we'd been fighting a losing battle, especially in places like Tangley where every copse and hedge seemed bursting with rabbits although I employed a man full time trapping, gassing and ferreting. The only month he did anything else but kill rabbits was during harvest and yet the rabbits were still winning.

Much of the hedge destruction which people complained about was a move to destroy rabbit breeding-colonies, for the losses we suffered were immeasurable. The Ministry of Agriculture calculated that the damage to cereal, kale, root and grass crops caused by rabbits cost the country over fifty million pounds a year in lost food production. Against this the direct income from rabbits was only about two million pounds a year, including the trade in by-products such as fur and felt.

Myxomatosis has kept rabbit numbers right down to the great benefit of farmers and foresters. Those rabbits that do survive now seem to live on top of the ground for most of the year, in woods and hedges; when they breed they dig solitary holes, or stops, in the middle of fields. If and when they do congregate in colonies in burrows, they are soon wiped out, for the rabbit fleas, which are the vectors for the disease, spread quickly through crowded groups.

I know that many are sad to see rabbits on the wane but there does seem a desire among some people to encourage the preservation of quite harmful species. I am sure that if there were still a few wolves loose in the mountains, the same people would excuse the occasional attacks on old women or children, as a small price to pay for the survival of a noble animal.

Some preservationists have too romantic a picture of the countryside. One result of the decline in the farming population is that rural England is now lived in by a great many non-farming types, commuters, the retired and weekenders, who seem to forget that large-scale intensive livestock production is an industry not an idyllic occupation. One farmer I know sold a row of dilapidated cottages for reconstruction but the new owner soon complained bitterly that his pigs smelt. She moaned on about this so much that the farmer eventually installed a huge scent-dispensing machine which was activated every time the wind switched round to blow in her direction. 'Does she like the scent you blow?' I enquired. 'Well, I don't think she finds much to choose between attar of roses and my pigs,' was the reply. If people insist on living in the countryside, they must get used to the smells, develop adenoids or breathe through their mouths. The farms and the pigs were there first and the original owners of cottages, the farm labourers for whom they were built, never complained.

Farm labour now gets the full whack of four weeks' holiday with pay, together with all bank holidays. As there are three at this time of year, Christmas, Boxing Day and New Year's Day, the farm generally closes down for the best part of a fortnight so that the men can take these off, plus any days still owing to them from their four weeks' annual leave. On a pure arable farm this would be easy, just a matter of locking up the tractors, but in my case, the sheep and pigs have to be fed and this means overtime and organising a rota of reliefs and the consequent compensations for lost time-off.

Farmers are extremely lucky in their labour, partly because of the close relationship between employer and employee and partly because of the very small numbers in each unit (with six men I am a large-scale employer) which give little chance for the formation of militant unions. I would not however say that this is an ideal relationship, nor is it perhaps advantageous for the employees that most of them live in tied houses and so are not in as strong a position as other workers. On the other hand the occupation of a free house with a garden does give quite a substantial boost to their wages.

I am only able to employ so many because I own my farm and do not therefore have to pay the ever-increasing rents or land costs that tenants have to face. It is probable that within fifty years there will be no hired labour permanently employed on farms. The great bulk of work will become the responsibility of the farmer and his family. Any extra help needed, for instance with milking, will be contracted out; the man being paid a set rate for the job rather than an annual wage.

This is already the pattern in most of Europe and in the temperate overseas countries like America and Australia. This does not mean a return to a nation of small-holders for, with modern machinery and techniques, one man alone can look after three or four hundred acres of grain or a herd of a hundred cows. But the high price of land means that in seeking a margin on which to live, the only cost within the farmer's control is that of labour.

Reduction of labour has been the pattern at Tangley. At the end of the last war I was farming 1,200 acres and employing twenty-two men. Today on less than 1,000 acres, I have six men but the value and volume of my output is many times what it was in the 1940s, thanks to improvements in the productivity of crops and stock and the use of new techniques. Of course my machinery was less efficient in those days and I was also compelled to grow labour-intensive crops like potatoes and flax for linen.

There was no deliberate policy of turning people off, I just did not replace those who left. Fortunately during those years there was plenty of work outside farming and the unions kept up a ceaseless barrage of propaganda against farm work which did have some effect in reducing the numbers coming forward. I must own that I have never had any difficulty in finding good workers, but it is not an easy job to retain them; constant application is needed to keep everyone sweet-tempered, particularly in bad weather. My technique is to make each individual, be he shepherd, pigman or maintenance man, responsible for his particular section. I encourage each of them to keep his own time and to develop his unit as if he was on his own. This does mean having to shut my eyes to tasks which I would prefer to be done rather differently, but the object of the exercise is the profit at the end, not the way in which it is reached. If my technique keeps me in reasonable comfort and allows me to re-equip the farm as I wish, there can't be much wrong with it.

I started the contractor system in my dairying soon after the war. The milker was paid at the rate of so much a gallon of milk produced and out of this total wage, he had to pay his helper, if he had one. This meant that I knew exactly how much the labour-cost of my milk amounted to and could do my budgeting

on that basis. I had to watch that the milker did not feed the cows too heavily with expensive compounds, but that was solved by looking after the feed-mill myself. I had the same cowman for much of the time and he told me once that it was like having a herd of his own. I built the house he lived in and he used his earnings, which amounted to double what he would have earned in paid employment, to buy it off me at cost. One of the few sensible actions of my life.

Although I have tried hard I have never managed to get the rest of my farming on the same basis. There are so many factors which can be right out of the man's, or even the farmer's, control which materially affect results. I have tried bonuses based on pigs sold or lambs reared but even these output-standards can be altered because I have not grown enough feed for the sheep or the pigs. Nor do I believe in overall profit sharing. This is because a farm's profit is almost impossible to define with any accuracy. Much of it is made up of the increases in value of crops and stock as yet unsold. Sale prices for these can vary enormously, and much depends on the farmer's abilities as a salesman, and the prices themselves can be affected by factors right outside his control.

There is undoubtedly an element of exploitation in all employee re-lationships; I only employ men in order to make a profit on my farm so I can claim no virtue in being a good employer because they stay with me for years. One or two have left to better themselves and become farm foremen, but several, including Stanley Nokes, have stayed until their retirement.

Stan came to me as a cowman at the beginning of my second year of farming in 1934. He had left school at eleven, on the outbreak of the first world war, and had learnt to plough with horses; he then worked as a cowman. The farmer who introduced me to him said that I could keep him for a year or so but then he would like Stan to come back to him as he would by then have secured possession of another farm. Instead however we have stayed together. Stan looked after my cows until the second world war started, when he asked if he might return to arable work to which I agreed. He managed this sector of my farm, which at one time amounted to 2,000 acres, most efficiently. We seldom discussed anything at length, I would give him a list of fields to be planted, buy the seeds and fertilisers and would see to it that he had enough men and machinery, then I left him to get on with it. He always had an uncanny instinct for working land and whatever the weather, however soon or however late the season, he always managed to get his acreage planted, and planted well. This must have been the result of working as a horse-ploughman with his feet quite literally on the ground for all those years.

Stan was not the most tactful of managers and used to complain to me about the men he had under him. 'Stan,' I used to say, 'be sensible. Remember, if they had as much sense as you and I have, we would be working for them and not them for us.'

Many farms are run by their foremen whilst the owners occupy themselves elsewhere. A Scottish friend of mine was taken away from school aged twelve as unteachable. He would not work at home either so, in desperation, his exasperated parents set him up in a small farm where he immediately flourished. When I last stayed with him, he had a most complicated set-up including cereals, cows, tomatoes, carnations, pigs and vegetables. Grudgingly he took me round his farm at my insistence, before he went off for a day's salmon-fishing, an occupation which exhausted him for nine months of the year. He seldom rose until eleven a.m. and only looked in on the farm if there were visitors or a major disaster. Farmers have always been lucky in the type of man who works up to be foreman.

December is the season for the fatstock shows which flourish up and down the country, culminating in two major ones, that in Edinburgh and the Smithfield Show at Earl's Court in London. Their origin goes back to the bad old days, before systems of keeping animals through the winter were evolved and before the days of refrigeration, when much of the livestock used to be slaughtered for food before it starved to death, thus making a virtue out of necessity.

This slaughter used to start before the end of October and from then until Christmas people were very well fed indeed, but after that fresh meat was scarce until the grass began to grow again; from January until the spring, people had to eat salted-down or smoked meat. Having eaten salt beef at sea and salt mutton in an economical New Zealand household, I can emphatically say that things are now much improved.

The efficient winter feeding of livestock is of fairly recent date; it originated on the Continent where they learnt to store turnips and other roots for long periods for winter feeding. These root crops also fattened animals well which removed the need for wholesale winter slaughter, but it still left the commercial attractions of supplying a Christmas market to be exploited.

Christmas fatstock shows have followed the same pattern for many years. Farmers parade their beasts to show off their beauty and then butchers bid for them. If a butcher buys the champion he also gets a picture of the beast to hang up in his shop beside the carcass which, particularly if the beast was well covered in suet, will be very handsome. Unfortunately, although the housewife likes to look at a fine suet-rounded beast, she doesn't like to eat one; she won't pay best beef prices for her meat if it is too fatty.

Judging live animals at these shows is really a beauty contest, based on superficial standards, rather like the human contests of this kind, which also leave the inner worth to chance. Everyone likes a nicely rounded body with a straight back and good legs which stride out well, but unfortunately this tells us nothing about the proportion of lean to fat.

The object of fatstock shows is of course to persuade farmers to produce better-class animals. It is how breeders advertise their wares. But even before the war these show-standards were coming under attack from the scientific fringe. These critics contended that what mattered was not conformation alone but a good conversion-rate of feed into saleable meat, the production of carcasses without excessive fat, and shortening the time of growth to slaughter-weight. All these are hereditary factors which can be recorded and the answers used to indicate which lines of breeding-stock should be followed. This started with broilers in the USA and with pigs in Denmark. The results achieved have completely altered the performance of these species. They now grow to marketing size in a fraction of the time they used to take. Nothing like the same results have yet been achieved with beef and sheep. But the reproductive cycle of a chicken is six months, a pig one year, sheep two years and beef-cattle nearly three years.

I don't support live shows, but more to encourage my shepherd and pigman than anything else, I do enter for carcass shows. All my livestock is sold by grade and deadweight and so I have to choose the stock that I send in for these shows when it's alive. I used to think I was rather good at this, particularly with sheep, and could, I thought, estimate the resulting carcass very well. But I was wrong. Like judges of the human body, farmers, and even butchers, don't know much about the make-up of an animal under the skin.

There are problems with the judges too. Two years ago the winners of the sheep carcasses at the local show were very fat indeed. So last year I sent in sheep which I was sure would please the same judges. Unfortunately I did not realise that the judges had been changed; I did not come back with even a second or third prize. However I did win a silver cup with a pig which I did not even choose myself. I sent a load to the slaughter-house and just told the lorry-driver to enter the first ten off the lorry into the competition. The next year we tried to keep the cup and took a great deal of trouble over our entry. We got nowhere.

By selling all my pigs and lambs on the hook after slaughter, I know what the price per pound is going to be before they leave the farm. The animals only have to make one journey which saves them considerable stress and I save the auctioneer's commission and some transport. This also saves the animals much knocking about in markets. All in all I get a fair price, but it is one based on the prices ruling in the live markets on the day of sale. I may miss out on a

particularly good market, but I avoid some bad ones. I also miss the satisfaction of standing behind a good pen of animals and gloating over my neighbours when I have beaten them by a pound or two a head.

I enjoy going to the occasional show, both local and national; they are great places for swapping information, seeing friends and having a good gossip. I have been going to Smithfield Show for many years now, even when it was held in the old Agricultural Hall at Islington before the war. It was here that the great glycerine scandal occurred. The Show had been honoured with a visit by King George VI, and when admiring a winning beast His Majesty pressed his fingers on the animal's rump to feel, as he was advised, the firmness of the flesh. To everyone's horror the royal fingerprints remained embedded in the flesh and to solve the mystery the animal was slaughtered. It was found that someone had injected glycerine under the skin to fill up a few low places. It was a work of great skill, but the winner had to be disqualified, and its owner admonished. Does this still happen today? I don't know. But I don't believe race-horse doping has been wiped out yet either.

But the support of the Smithfield Show is no longer the livestock, which is relegated to the draughty corridors of Earl's Court. Machinery now occupies pride of place as it pays the rent. In my fifty years of farming I have seen the transition from the horse to the tractor. A marvellous time to have lived through and at one time I used to travel long distances to see new machines, but sadly, static exhibitions of machinery no longer thrill me.

Today all machines work well; they do what they are supposed to do but they cost so much that the very thought of buying a new one fills me with horror. The list price of my new combine-harvester is nearly £30,000. A new four-wheel-drive tractor is £21,000 and a two-wheel-drive £11,000. Plough-shares, which I used to buy by the tonne, I now buy by the piece and a new weighing-machine for pigs now costs £400 against the old £50. So my principle with machinery is to keep it as young as I can afford, so that if the worst happens and cereal prices go down through the floor, I shall not have to buy a new tractor, combine-harvester or anything else for at least ten years.

As the year comes to an end, like most farmers, I take stock of my financial position. Indigestion after a heavy Christmas dinner is a potent stimulus to financial worry. We have all been made more conscious of budgeting by various advisory agencies and I can tie myself up in knots trying to work out a cash-flow position for many months ahead. I never consciously budget in a true sense. You cannot for instance budget the cost of a crop, because the season may force you to perform extra field operations. You may need extra sprays, the harvest may be bad with doubled drying costs. Yields may be 20 or 30 per cent below target. So if you budget you must allow for an enormous profit on exaggerated costs. If your budget cannot show you such a result, you might as well sell the farm or give up budgeting. I prefer the latter course. A good mood in which to approach the New Year.

January

I always think myself lucky if I reach the New Year without having to give the sheep hay or compound feed. The climate in southern England is usually sufficiently mild to keep the grass, if not growing, green enough to interest the ewes until the New Year, provided there is no snow, in which case getting them fed over the prolonged holiday period can be expensive in overtime. But the next few weeks are crucial to a successful lamb crop so I must watch their feed intake carefully.

As the ewes are more than halfway through their pregnancy, the lambs are making increasingly heavy demands on their resources. The embryos' weights increase from about ½ lb to as much as 10 lbs in the next few weeks and if the ewes cannot nourish them from their daily intake of fodder, they have to draw on their own body systems. The effect of any sudden change in diet at this point, or an imbalance of nutrition, can be quite literally staggering. About forty years ago there was a bad January snowfall after a very mild early winter. My ewes, which were in tiptop condition and still living off grass, found their food supply suddenly cut off, deep under snow, so I had to feed them hay and compound feed. They ate these all right, but suddenly began to lose interest in food and everything else, going into a comatose condition. One morning I found that about one in five of them was sitting or standing with its head on one side as if listening to some angel choir; they took no notice of me when I came up to them, their eyes were open, but they did not close them at my touch. I had never seen this condition before, nor had my veterinary surgeon, whom I summoned at once. He got busy on the telephone and came up with the information that this was pregnancy toxaemia, caused by a break in the continuity of the food supply just as the ewes were beginning to feel the drain of their pregnancy. The sudden arbitrary nature of a change of diet had completely upset the sheeps' metabolism.

Attacks of this kind were apparently quite common in the border areas of England and Scotland and, as they generally coincided with a snowfall, the illness was known as snow-blind, dunt, or sometimes twin-lamb disease, because it was most likely to affect ewes carrying twins. Once a ewe has been affected, there is little that can be done to save her unless she aborts, in which case she usually recovers. If an attack is spotted early on it may be possible to cure some animals by injecting glucose under the skin but a farmer may have many sheep collapse at once, in which case he will be hard put to save heavy losses. In extreme cases I have known half a flock die, but have never been so unlucky myself, although I have a few cases every year.

As sheep farming has intensified in the south of England and more flocks have suffered pregnancy toxaemia, various techniques to stave it off have been tried. One suggestion is to give the sheep exercise, making them range over a very big pasture, another is to feed them at the opposite end of the field to the water trough, but the real answer is to change to dry feeding early on in the ewes' pregnancy and to see that they get plenty of water.

At one time it was believed that sheep needed very little water and many flocks seemed to survive without any, but in those days sheep were usually being fed on turnips or other roots, which would have had a high moisture content, as has grass. But if frost hardens the grass, ponds freeze over and the only feed is hay or other dry foodstuffs, then sheep will draw on their body systems for moisture with dire results. Before I realised this, some of my ewes would lose weight very rapidly, the flesh would literally seem to melt from their bones during periods of heavy frost. I once had to get rid of a shepherd who would not see that the ice in the water troughs was broken every day and who allowed my flock to get very thin.

Sheep will winter far better on snow-covered ground than they will when it is iron-hard and dry because they can at least get some moisture from eating snow. Evidently horses are the same for I once kept some Argentine polo ponies throughout a very bad winter. They had water available but we never saw them drink and although we led them to water they would not touch it. I was very worried about them, but they gained weight all through the winter and sold well the following spring.

I used to have endless trouble with pregnancy toxaemia, especially when I lambed late in March. Now I start lambing in mid-February, although this is a long time before the grass arrives. But it does mean that the period when the ewes are at risk from snow-blind is much shorter. I also begin now to offer extra food early on in January and try to make the compound feed match the development of the lambs, starting with a few ounces per ewe a day and gradually ending with around a pound and a half in the week before lambing. The final result should be a ewe in good condition with a full udder of milk and her lambs strong and healthy when born.

But not all sheep will eat dry feed willingly. I once kept mountain ewes bought in mid-Wales which were small, white-faced, quite prolific and extraordinarily good mothers, never abandoning their lambs. But they did not like confinement, and didn't like to be hand-fed; they would climb out of almost any field and a proportion would never eat hay or other feed. These were the ones which died. I tried all manner of tricks to make them eat, from shutting them up in barns or yards for a while, to starting the feed early in the year. But in the end, the only way to help them to survive was to give them the run of the farm, for they would always find a living of some sort, even if it was in a neighbour's garden. Their straying powers were so well known that when some exasperated farmers had taken legal proceedings against a neighbour who let his Welsh ewes run all over the county, the judge laid it down in open court that bringing Welsh sheep to Wiltshire should be an indictable offence.

If ewes were shut indoors during much of the winter, it is true that they might get used to the dry feed early on, but there are two main objections to this: they would not get any grazing which costs very little, and, more important, they would be at great risk from disease, because animals kept inside are jammed so close together. The most likely illness to break out would be salmonella, because there are always one or two carriers in any group of animals. As a salmonella attack can cut the lamb crop in half, I have always decided not to risk shutting my sheep in, even when they won't eat dry feed. This is a confession of failure because some farmers manage to house their ewes quite successfully.

Some people house sheep during the winter, not only to control their feed, but also because they can make such an awful mess of a pasture in wet weather, by trampling it into such a morass that the grass will not grow again for a long time. But sheep do not really need a house or roof over their heads; they are perfectly insulated against both heat and cold by their fleeces and would winter perfectly well on concrete without overhead shelter.

At this stage you may well ask, how do hill ewes like the Swaledale or the Welsh manage in their natural habitat when there is a heavy frost, the ground is iron-hard and all water frozen solid? The short answer is that they don't very well. They seldom give birth to twins and a number appear to be barren. The ewes seem to have become pregnant initially but when the supply of nutrition failed, they either ingested the tiny embryos into their systems or aborted. This of course is nature's way of ensuring the survival of the population to match the feed available.

If it is a bitter cold January, not much can be accomplished on the land except to feed the stock and break the ice in the water troughs. It is a quiet time for farmers, a moment when they can catch up on their accounts, their reading and the latest trends and techniques. A frivolous few may go skiing or cruising but most of us now begin to indulge our craving for endless discussion.

One of the strangest aspects of farming is the way in which individual farmers give away their most rewarding professional secrets to their neighbours and competitors. A man has only to discover how to grow an extra hundredweight of grain per acre, or how to gain a few more gallons of milk per cow, or extra pigs per sow, and he will advertise it to all and sundry, through the farming press or on radio or television.

Like most farmers, I take notice of these developments, motor hundreds of miles to look at them, often scoff, but am never too proud to copy, if I think it will pay. I could happily spend a good part of the summer looking at 'on farm' demonstrations of new techniques, and the winters going to conferences to talk about them.

Conferences come under several headings. There are at least a score of individual farmer-interest groups ranging from the Agricultural Economics Society to the Pig Health Association. Then there are conferences instituted by those exploiting the industry for gain, amongst which I must include the banks, fertiliser, feeding-stuffs and machinery interests. Advisory services are well in the act, with what might be called 'ethical conferences' on all manner of subjects; these take particular care not to advertise anything at all but to me they are always suspect as they push a government line.

Then there are conferences organised purely and simply by farmers for farmers. Paramount among these is the Oxford Farming Conference, which is held every January. It is a magnificent baring of souls and systems; farmers detail their successes and will mention their failures; world figures are induced to come at their own expense and expound. Those attending come from all over the British Isles, delighted to have the opportunity to meet each other, to swap information and to talk farming for about sixteen hours a day while staying in the rudimentary comfort of an Oxford college. I have been to most of the conferences over the last thirty years and even addressed it on three occasions. The organisers publish the proceedings in book form and it is a most salutary experience to read the speeches of yesteryear; so confidently delivered yet so frequently completely falsified by events.

The fact that farmers are so free with their most successful discoveries when most other professions cloak theirs in the deepest secrecy, is a strange sidelight on farmers' contradictory natures. The whole object of these conferences is to disseminate information on how to produce more and more food. Yet every farmer knows, or should do from his mother's knee, that the more food produced, the lower falls the price and the worse off the farmer. The organisers realise this of course and conferences on marketing occupy a fair bit of the winter talking-season. These are much less precise affairs than those on production. After all it is not very difficult to prove to people that if you apply a measured amount of energy, fertiliser and seed to a piece of ground you will get, within limits, a reasonable enough return, and that there are combinations of the inputs which can be adjusted to increase production further. What is less clearly stated is the point at which the law of diminishing returns begins to operate: when is the extra cost not recouped from extra yield? Nor in all the dozens of conferences I have attended has anyone told me how to make sure that the market for my expanding production will itself expand to accommodate it.

I must have listened to dozens of hectoring speeches from the leaders of the greatest retailing organisations in this country, telling me to produce what the consumer wants, in shape, size, quality or whatever, and exhorting me to have everything graded within narrow limits, which generally mean the standards of that particular buyer. But these people will never be tied down to stating exactly and precisely what they would be prepared to pay for such excellence. Buyers will never even lay down in advance the price around which they would be prepared to fix a quality-scheme. This is because all our prices are in the end dependent on the market; this particularly affects the higher-quality products, which are where premiums are earned. The basic prices we receive are at present guaranteed by the Common Agricultural Policy, but this only acts as a safety-net if the total market is oversupplied. If supplies are short, there is a strong market in which quality standards matter little. But should the market be oversupplied there is very little in the way of premiums at all.

One cannot blame the ultimate buyers for exploiting this situation once they get the chance. They are only human. But it comes a bit hard when they lecture farmers for exploiting the market when it is short. The only way in which markets can operate free of supply and demand is to have a complete monopoly selling-organisation which channels all sales through its own bottleneck, such as the Milk Marketing Board. I think this has done a good job because I can remember the chaos that existed in the milk industry before its formation in 1933 when the buyers had more than the upper hand. Many farmers would like to see the same system applied to other products, to cereals, pig-meat, eggs and lambs for example, but although one or two boards were formed, they failed, either because they did not get acceptance by the farmers, or because the government of the day would not allow them to have completely monopoly powers. Today only the Wool Board remains, besides the Milk Board, which is threatened by EEC legislation.

A monopoly would be essential because unfortunately farmers are seldom loyal to their fellow-farmers in any collective enterprise. Before the Milk Board was formed there were many attempts to band farmers together to present buyers with a united front. They always failed because in spite of fervent public declarations of support for holding out for a price, these were always broken by some individuals settling for less. It is this lack of loyalty which has prevented the development of the co-operative principle in British farming. In other countries farmers co-operate because either they are intimidated by their fellows or they have had such a bad time in the hands of the trade that they are driven to doing so.

About ten years ago I read that farmers in west Brittany were rioting because they were being exploited by the wicked vegetable merchants. As a keen student of such affairs, I went over to France, only to find that the truth was very different. The farmers were rioting all right, with broccoli heads spilt all over the road, but the objectives of the riot were not the wicked merchants, but those farmers who would not join the local co-operative. These dissident individualists were being ambushed by the co-operators and prevented from selling their produce. Soon after the riots, the French government enforced co-operative membership, since which time all Breton farmers have remained united; compulsion being sugared by bribes in the way of subsidies and better markets. I don't know if the traders were bullying the farmers into the co-op in the first place or not, but the farmers were certainly bullying the independents. So far British farmers have not suffered enough to forego their independence to buy and sell as they please.

I know exactly how the individualists feel and would be prepared to defend this freedom up to, but not beyond, the bounds of common sense. Like most of my fellows, I enjoy buying and selling and I never think that the employee of a co-operative can make a better deal for me than I can make for myself. If I think I have made a good bargain, I am very pleased with myself, and if I have not, I don't talk about it.

It is this independent competitive spirit which supports the British livestock markets. We enjoy going to market, meeting our friends and arguing about those aspects of farming that the more élitist among us have been pondering in places like the Oxford Conference. I use the term élitist advisedly because there are a few farmers who like to think of themselves as the leaders of the industry. They are not necessarily in the National Farmers' Union, in fact many profess to scorn it. They are the ones seeking to distance themselves from the muddy-boot farmer type and in their own terms are succeeding very well. The reason for this arrogance is that the average mixed farm is hardly big enough to contain the mental and physical energy of the owner. He is not prepared to operate within the confines of his own boundaries; he wants to expand, to use big machines, to move people about; often he has the capacity to be a captain of industry and is frustrated. He shows his less able neighbours just what he thinks of them and they resent it. So you find farmers almost aggressively demanding that their neighbours follow their example, while at the same time busily trying to get the best of them in every possible way. We are far from being one big happy family.

Some farmers relieve their frustrations by enlarging their holdings, renting extra bits of land here and there or by buying additional farms. However Britain is almost completely alone in Europe where this can be done. Elsewhere labour-costs inhibit expansion beyond what can be accomplished by the farmer and his family, and there is a definite bias against farm enlargement, enforced in many cases by law. Although the Treaty of Rome lays down that an EEC citizen may live, work, buy and sell property in any member country, just try to buy a farm in France. Only a Frenchman may farm there and every deal has to be passed through SAFER, an organisation which controls all farm occupancy. There is also a limit to the size of enterprise which can be bought or built up and SAFER can annul any purchase, even one made in good faith. Roughly the same situation also applies in Germany and Denmark. In these countries farms and farming are reserved for the farming population and no one man or industrialist or institution is able to aggrandise his holding simply by the use of his chequebook.

French farms have always been smaller than British ones because under the Code Napoléon, which still applies for the most part, a man's property when he dies is divided equally between his heirs. This may lead to absurd fragmentation of holdings but it also means that everyone keeps to this law because all have something to gain from it. The eldest son usually farms the land and if possible he persuades his siblings to sell or rent their portions to him, but all the family maintain a vested interest in what goes on back at the family homestead, which swells the farming vote enormously. The basis of Europe's present agricultural prosperity is this powerful lobby of small-scale farmers and their relations who can make hell for the politician in a way large-scale farmers never can. All European governments therefore support their farmers in a way no British government ever does. Farmers in Britain form about 2 per cent of the population but 8 per cent in France and Germany, rising to 20 per cent if you include all the extended family members.

Whilst Napoleon was rampaging over Europe promulgating his useful Code, Britain was hedging her fields after the Enclosure Acts, driving farm labourers and small-holders into factories and towns, enlarging the size of farms and seeing that they remained large through the exercise of primogeniture. West Germany saw something similar happening in the 1950s, for quite different reasons, over the wall in East Germany, where tiny farms were being amalgamated into collectives and the rural peasant was being encouraged into the towns. West Germany did not want that to happen, as it thought proletarianisation of the land was bad for society, so it brought industry to the countryside. Families can maintain a rural way of life on their small-holdings but earn extra

47

money by working part-time in nearby factories. This has been extremely successful: most German farms are run by the family, output is high; more butter and beef go into EEC Intervention-buying from here than from anywhere else and production from German soils is rather better than that from a similar area of British land.

I don't think it would be a bad idea at all if British farms got a bit smaller. I am certainly against institutional farming by City interests where British financial concerns have bought land for investment purposes and tried to replace the traditional mixed farm by an industrial-type structure. Some of them have been

successful but others have come rather unstuck. Corporate management does not seem to respond well to the climate and other vagaries which are best met by an individual farmer working on his own small patch.

I am not denying that there are of course many large and successful farm businesses whose prosperity depends on the drive and genius of their founder, but I do not think this trend will continue. Anyway few of them usually survive the founder's departure from the scene. I suspect the same applies in many walks of life. For instance, many of my generation came into farming just before – or just after – the last war when prices of land were rock bottom and so we were able to establish ourselves, as a result, on quite large acreages. But we were only able to do this because there was no real competition to go into farming. As farming had been in depression since the 1880s, briefly lifted by two world wars, everyone thought this would again be the pattern once normality returned. Quite a few sold out at the first faint lift in land prices, but I took the other view and became an owner instead of a tenant.

It was a step I never regretted, although I had to borrow all the money to buy my first farm. It was a rash step to take at the time because it ran counter to tradition. From time immemorial British land had been owned by relatively few landlords who let to tenant farmers, whom they guaranteed to support in bad times as well as good, even though they did not do very well financially out of the deal because rents were low. My friends told me that I would miss a good landlord for it was claimed to be an almost perfect partnership: the landlord provided the fixed capital, the land and the buildings and the tenant did his share by working the soil. In fact this relationship had only really been successful in Victorian times when much of England had been owned by families who had done well out of the Industrial Revolution and the exploitation of the Empire. They had made their money elsewhere and so were able as a result to support, there is no other word for it, an obsequious tenantry.

As it happened, my first landlord died very soon after I had taken over his farm and it was sold to an individual who went bankrupt. I was given a year's notice to quit. I then took on the tenancy of another farm, only to have the same difficulties repeated five years later: the landlord went bankrupt and gave me notice. I gave this farm up, too, but it took me seven years to obtain the compensation to which I was entitled for disturbance of my tenancy.

This second blow, because it *was* a blow to a young man, made me decide to buy my own house away from the farm. I then took on an increasing amount of land round and about as a tenant, eventually purchasing it all, finishing up with nearly 3,000 acres at an annual net land-cost of less than two pounds an acre with long-term loans at 4½ per cent. It has turned out to be very successful but in these operations I was guided by no economic considerations at all, only by a determination never again to put my tenancies at the risk of a landlord's idiosyncracies.

Many other farmers did the same as I did and bought their land. As a result the proportion of land rented in Britain has fallen from 90 per cent in 1910 to 38 per cent today; the depression, death-duties and capital-transfer tax have also encouraged much selling over the years. During this time, the image of the benevolent landlord succouring his tenant has given way to the reality of a business-like owner, individual or institutional, using every means to maximise his rents and get a proper return on the capital he has invested in the land.

I remember going to a land auction many years ago, where the purchaser was a local tenant farmer. I met his landlord there, who furiously declared that his tenant had come to him every year with a hard-luck story, seeking a rent rebate, which he, the generous landlord, had handsomely granted, and now the tenant had outbid him for the farm. That no longer happens.

Very few farms come up for rent these days and there are a number of reasons for this, among them, security for existing tenants and their families under the law, and the prosperity of farming which encourages landlords to take their farms in hand. Farm profits are also treated much more liberally taxwise than are rents, and there are other landlord benefits. Most farms let today are put out to competitive tender. Those who tender for tenancies are usually farmers who so desperately want the farm that they will bid what many consider to be an uneconomic price. But this depends on what you mean by economic. A rent which is possible for one man to pay, because of his ability, or his acceptance of a lower standard of living, might be out of the question for an established farmer on a much lower rent who is used to an easier tempo of life.

Under the Agricultural Holdings Act, it is possible to resist a landlord's

demands for a rent increase by going to arbitration. But the instructions to the arbitrator lay down that the rent fixed must accord with what a willing tenant will offer for similar land. It is easy then for the landlord or his agent, usually the latter, to put a farm on the tender-market and then use the results as evidence before the arbitrator.

The scarcity of farms to rent is also due in part to the virtual security of tenure granted to tenants which in certain cases can pass to two successors and so last for three generations. No private landlord is going to risk tying up his land for so long, so he either sells, or farms the place himself.

The Young Farmers' Clubs have joined with the landlords to try to persuade the government to break the security provisions so that they too one day can have the chance of renting a farm. This is fair enough but what they forget is that, even if they manage to prevent a son following his father, there is no certainty that the farm will be re-let and in any case there are only so many farms in the country and there can only be one man for each, whoever he is. This is a very far cry from the days when I first came to Tangley, when the landlord showed me some 200 acres at the far end of his estate and told me that I could only have the rest of the farm on condition I accepted this land rent-free and kept it tidy.

The lowest rent I ever paid was during the 1939 war. I was asked by the local War Agricultural Committee to take over a derelict farm; this was the body of local farmers who controlled farming in wartime. The landlord would not consider any bid from me for the rent of his badly-neglected land which did not even have a water supply; he said the Committee must set it, so they awarded it to me at five shillings (25p) an acre for the first two years and ten shillings (50p) an acre for the next two. I would have been prepared to pay one pound an acre but meekly accepted the rulings of the adjudicators, two substantial local farmers. A sensible rent for similar land today would be between thirty and forty pounds an acre depending on the buildings. A man desperate for land might bid over sixty pounds. Gross output in 1939 would perhaps have been ten pounds an acre but in 1981 it would be more likely to have been £200.

In France over 50 per cent of the land is rented, compared to our 38 per cent, because of the Code Napoléon. The eldest son usually gains the farmhouse and nearby land and then buys or rents all the property of his siblings, subject to SAFER, who can pre-empt the sale and allocate even a sibling's farm to someone else, if it so pleases. The inheritor can obtain special loans at low interest rates to make these purchases and, in addition, rents are fixed on a complicated formula which takes in, among other aspects, the quality of the land and the value for the year of the principal product. For example, if the land is believed to be worth a rent of five quintals a hectare (about half a tonne of wheat), then it would be priced at about fifty pounds a hectare. Generally the rents work out at about 10 per cent of the gross value of output. French holdings are usually limited to what one family could farm for themselves. The only way to participate in a French farm therefore is to marry a rich farmer's daughter. But beware, French women control the purse-strings.

I don't believe that any policy can provide more British farms to rent or buy until there is a change in the prosperity of farming. At present farmers have been largely insulated from the recession that is afflicting everyone else, so no one is going to give up a farm willingly nor will his family. The big influx of new blood which infiltrated during the pre-war years replaced those who had to leave the land because of the recession of the 20s. The impact of death-duties also got rid of many landlords and owner-occupiers. This is where I and many like me got their chance.

I believe that the two-hundred-acre one-man farm should be the future aim, but only economic or taxation forces can bring that change about. In any case the agricultural land area is bound to be reduced by the spread of towns and roads, and demands for recreation and conservation.

February

February is filled with feverish activity if the weather is mild. It is the time for sowing spring wheat and barley, for spraying the emerging autumn-sown crops against disease and for lambing.

Candlemas Day, February 2nd, is really the middle of winter. The wise farmer should have enough fodder left in his stores to keep his livestock through to the spring. This means at least as much as he has fed already. I am not always a wise farmer. I am an optimist and this is based on some lucky experiences in the past when spring has come early. I forget the times when grass has been delayed until the end of April and remember only the odd year when it was possible to cease hay-feeding at the beginning of March.

Sheep and cattle take a lot of satisfying. They much prefer grass to hay, particularly the rather indifferent hay that I am able to make, and as winter proceeds they seem to need increasing quantities to hold their body weight; I think it is something to do with daylight hours. An old friend told me once that his cattle never began to improve, however much he fed them, until there were at least twelve hours of daylight, which in the south of England happens around the end of February.

The climate of Hampshire is fairly favourable with the chance of a very short cold season, so I don't have to make provision for six or seven months without grass growth which those in the midlands and north of Britain have to consider. Farmers up there have to make absolutely certain that they have a plentiful supply of hay and silage, that it is well made and nutritious, and that their buildings are laid out in such a way that the stock can be comfortably kept off the land if necessary.

Even then, however, they don't practise indoor husbandry more than they have to because it is expensive. It is perfectly possible to formulate a complete ration, based on cereals made into cow-cake or nuts with added vitamins and proteins, which will give animals a constant well-balanced diet, designed for the highest production of both milk and meat, which they can live on for months at a time. Indeed, keeping animals permanently off the fields on such rations is well established in Canada and northern Europe and used to be much more popular here.

Before the war, I was able to buy cattle feed so cheaply that I could step up the supply of nuts to my animals whenever I liked and could disregard the date of grass growth or the failure of hay supplies. But the economics of this has been upset by the high price of cereals which form the basic ingredient of the compound feed. To give an example, in 1939 I had made a contract to buy cattle-compound cake at six pounds a tonne. My milk sold for the equivalent of six pence a gallon. Today's price for the same compound cake is £136 a tonne while the price of milk is fifty-five pence a gallon. Feed costs have gone up nearly twenty-three times while the price of milk has only risen by ten times.

The same calculations can be applied to feed for sheep and other livestock which explains the pressure on farmers to improve the quality of their home-grown fodder crops. Every year when I see my sheep turning up their noses at my indifferently made hay I resolve that next time I will do better. A resolution which it is much easier to make than to keep. However, unlike the foolish virgins in the parable I can usually buy my way out of trouble . . . at a price.

February brings sowing fever. It is a disease to which arable farmers are particularly prone and can be brought on by the sound of a neighbour's tractors working when one's own are not. Farming is very competitive, and the need to

54

be first in everything is paramount. There is also a theory, not borne out by any scientific results, that the earlier spring cereals are sown, the better they yield.

Theoretically I try to be a philosopher in these matters, pretending to believe, in public anyway, that there will always be plenty of time for sowing. But in practice I am just as competitive, and as prone to entering the race, as any of my neighbours. I begin to nag my foreman into having a look at the land almost every day. Particularly if I hear that someone in the next parish has got a few acres planted.

But my neighbours, especially those to the south of me, have advantages. Their soils in general are chalky and very friable. They can run over them with tractors and cultivators without harm. Even if it is wet when they do this, the soil will fall apart when it dries out. But my own soils are largely clay, mix them with water, puddle them about and you have bricks. It is all too easy for me to make bricks in the field instead of a good seedbed. Moving heavy machinery over the land at the wrong time will produce a collection of lumps in which no seed will be able to germinate.

What I need is a hard frost for a few days. Not just any old frost, but one which ends with a spell of dry weather, and not an inch or two of rain which will undo all the good the frost has done. I shall then be able to work the land when the soil just below the surface is still moist but not so wet that it will stick to the tractor wheels or the implements. It should be steadily drying all day long. I like the earth to be damp like brown sugar, but of course much finer; it will then provide a seedbed in which the roots can spread out and the shoots push through to the light. The plough is only one of the tools to be used, it buries the

existing trash from the surface, or it could be old turf. The underside of the furrow exposed after ploughing can then be worked about with a variety of implements ranging from harrows to discs. Generally the fewer the times you need to work the land the better, but the amount of working cannot be determined in advance.

The main difference between now and the days when I started with horses is that I can do the work so much more rapidly. For instance, one man with a team of horses might harrow eight acres a day but with a medium tractor he can do fifty to sixty acres and if necessary work all night. Horses can work no longer than can men.

It is essential to get these operations just right, or you can get in an awful mess. I used at one time to roll the fields after sowing in order to push the flints down, out of the way of the combine knife. I rolled one field myself, as I remember it on an Easter Sunday. Unfortunately the texture of the soil had gone from drying to dampening and the passing of the roller caused the top to seal or cap. It then became dry and the cap so hard that it was impossible for the germinating barley to get through to the surface. The whole field had to be ploughed up and resown. An expensive lesson to be more careful in future. Perhaps it would have been better had I not laboured on the Sabbath.

Sunday work is almost universal now at peak periods, but when I started farming it was unheard of. Cows were milked and stock fed of course, but anything like regular farm work was condemned. I once got up at four a.m. on a Sunday morning to mow an isolated field which I thought would be well away from prying eyes. But by midday three of my neighbours had rung up and complained that my tractor had disturbed their slumbers. Luckily the men accept that we could not manage without Sunday work at peak periods in our uncertain climate, indeed most of them value the extra overtime pay.

February used to be a time of tension: there was so much sowing to be done yet the weather was seldom helpful; now the fashion is for more autumn sowing so there is less pressure on spring work. I say fashion, for farming practice goes in phases just like ladies' fashion. Perhaps the best example of this can be seen in dairying. When I was a boy all cows were kept in for the seven winter months, tied by the neck in cow-stalls. Then there was a fashion for keeping them in the open all the year round and milking them from portable sheds. Next they were brought under cover again and kept in what was called loose housing and bedded on straw. After that they were put into individual stalls or cubicles without neck-yokes. The cows voluntarily went into their cubicles to lie down or chew the cud. But some cows refused to do that and lay on the passage floors behind the cubicles and so got very dirty. Now the very latest fashion is to put a chain across the back of each cubicle to keep each cow in her right place. The most likely next move will be a neck-chain once again. Had I therefore continued to use the system of neck-yoking which my predecessor at my first farm was using way back in the 1920s, I should by now be back in the van of progress.

Will the present pressure for autumn sowing be another ephemeral fad? Advantages in yield, particularly with barley, have to be set against the disadvantages of having to hurry to get the land ready and planted in the autumn when the days are getting shorter all the time. Everyone involved feels the strain, including the merchants who have to race to process the seed-corn which has just been harvested. I feel that at the moment I have managed to distribute my energies fairly evenly between spring and autumn, so that neither time is too hectic if the weather is kind, but it takes very little to upset this precarious balance.

February is the time to look closely at the newly-emerging autumn-sown crops to see if they show signs of stress, disease or lack of nitrogen. If I think they do, should I go ahead and spray in the hopes that the chemicals I give them will be successful or do I try to save money and hope that they will recover of their own accord? The problem is further complicated by the lack of knowledge at the moment about how effective chemical sprays are. Some people ask an adviser to come in to help them with their decision. But to be told by a young man, no older than one of my grandchildren, that I ought to spray, which could cost me many pounds an acre, because he feels it would be a good idea, even though he cannot be sure it's necessary or will give me a certain return on my money, seems to me to be a most insane proposition. I prefer to make up my own mind. I try to recognise the disease or fungus and then select what I hope is the right chemical to apply. The trouble is that chemical farming is still in its infancy: no one really knows its cost-effectiveness. Many of the substances work well in laboratory conditions or on plants in greenhouses but do not perform so well in the fields. As with human beings, the reactions of living organisms vary infinitely according to the conditions of growth and the environment at the time of application.

I hate spending money unnecessarily because I have always found that the way to get on in life is not to throw cash around. I have tried therefore to acquire as much knowledge as I can about chemicals, but the experts cannot agree. There was a period when we were recommended to apply chemicals as prophylactics, as an insurance against disaster. Then another group of advisers came up with the theory that such applications might even stimulate the production of spores of various diseases. Yet others believed that the way to avoid disaster was to breed varieties which were resistant to the main diseases. There have been some quite good advances in this field, especially against rust which used to be an endemic plague on wheat, world-wide. The crop would die prematurely, the leaves went red and the grain that survived would be thin and pinched.

In Australia I once saw a field so affected by rust that the farmer had not even bothered to harvest it, all one thousand acres. But rust resistance, even when bred into a variety, can be undermined by the adaptability of the attacking pathogen. There have been several cases over the years of successful rust-resistant strains suddenly losing their resistance and succumbing to the disease in a big way. Once a crop loses its resistance, there is little to be done except to vow never to grow that species again because the chemicals used against slight attacks are all but powerless against a complete infection. I am careful to grow three separate varieties of wheat each year, choosing them because of their resistance to particular diseases and I make sure that they are unable to cross-infect one another.

Before the days of chemical insecticides and fungicides, which were only a decade ago, the choice of whether to spray or not didn't exist so my attention was not distracted all February by thinking whether I should be spraying or sowing on what few fine days there were. As it was not possible to do much about the many pests and diseases, it was not much use worrying. However I have always been able to do something to increase the nitrogen content of my soil.

Centuries ago, man realised that nitrogen was crucially important for plant growth and knew that it was stored in the root nodules of clover and also existed in most soils. He knew that clover would enrich the soil for the next year, which was why clover was planted before wheat in the rotation systems.

Nitrogen is in the air around us as a gas: certain bacteria in the soil convert this nitrogen in the air into nitrogenous compounds in the soil which dissolve in water. As these components are a waste product of the bacteria, excess is available for the benefit of plants and other soil organisms. Plants absorb the nitrogen through their root-hairs, along with water. Without nitrogen, plants would not be able to form proteins.

Clover and certain other plants, such as beans, possess special bacteria in the nodules which can directly fix nitrogen from the air. In New Zealand pastures are usually a mixture of clover and rye-grass, which ensures that there is always enough nitrogen being released into the soil by the clover to enable the rye-grass to flourish. As a result New Zealand has the reputation, which is well deserved, of being the best grassland country in the world. Moreover this grass grows well for ten or eleven months of the year. I can get the same sward at Tangley but only for a month or two. Because of the lower soil temperatures in England, the clover does not release its excess nitrogen until the middle of June. If I had to rely on naturally produced nitrogen, I should have to reduce my stocks of sheep and feed them much more in the way of compound feed to get my lambs fat, for my pastures would be pretty bare until late summer. As I am always deeply pessimistic and feel that there may come a day when purchased nitrogen runs out, I still sow a little wild white clover with every pasture. These plants, which are at present all but obliterated, will then be able to come back into their own and make the superbly balanced sward of my youth.

In order to have plenty of good grass earlier in the year, I begin to apply a nitrogen fertiliser in mid-February and then continue to repeat the application regularly until July. Nitrogen fertiliser zips up the plant-growth rate: it is like giving whisky to a tired man. Unlike whisky, however, it is not in any way harmful. The actual effect of nitrogen, in layman's language, is to combine with the other basic fertilisers, potash and phosphate, to make all the plant-food suddenly digestible to the growing crop. It could be said that nitrogen makes the top grow, phosphate encourages the roots and potash hastens ripening and maturing. However it is not much good applying nitrogen prematurely in the autumn as it would be leached away during the heavy winter rains: the more it poured, the more my application would be diluted. If on the other hand, there is a period of very hard frost, the nitrogen would remain locked in the soil because plants cannot absorb nitrogen from the soil unless it is warm. Even synthetic nitrogen needs a soil temperature of at least 45° Fahrenheit before it can be effective. Natural nitrogen starts to be available to plant life as the earth warms up on mild February days, so I aim to top-dress my autumn-sown crops and my pastures with a proportion of their spring ration about this time.

I use a liquid nitrogen fertiliser for my cereals because it is easy to handle and mixes well with a certain herbicide if necessary; in this way I can achieve two objectives with one application. I usually put on two doses of nitrogen during the spring, about a third of the whole amount in February and the balance at the end of March or in early April. But the time of application is dependent on the state of the land.

To give them a quick initial boost, spring-sown crops have much more nitrogen sown with the seeds than autumn ones have. Sowing fertiliser down the same spout as the seed is called combine-drilling and was first developed about forty years ago. When I first combine-drilled, the results were spectacular. I had taken over a derelict farm which hadn't been fertilised for years. I planted the seeds with a balanced fertiliser of high nitrogen content. That summer I could see from the difference in the crop, exactly to an inch where the fertiliser had run out.

Many people claim that the use of chemical fertilisers is unnatural and that crops grown with their help lack some essential ingredient: this makes them less valuable as human food. These people would prefer only natural fertilisers to be used, by which they mean human or animal manure or compost. I don't doubt these people's sincerity, but I would doubt that they have many facts with which to sustain their argument.

Chemicals such as phosphate and potash have been known and used on the land for centuries in countries all over the world. Phosphate used to be produced from bones, but there are not enough animals on earth today to provide all the bones needed for the vast areas under cultivation throughout the globe. Instead rock phosphate has to be used, either in its raw state, when it is very slow-acting, or broken down with sulphuric acid to form super phosphate, but there is no evidence to show that this reduces the value of the crop as food.

Two hundred years ago the old farming manuals recommended dressing the land with potash in its commonest form, salt. Those who complain should remember that yields of the main cereals have on average trebled in the last forty years through the improved varieties of seed and the use of new fertiliser

59

techniques. They might be rather hungry if farmers used only manure.

The first inhabitants of southern England farmed the downland soils for grain – the outlines of their fields can still be faintly traced on my own farm. But after hundreds of years, the land would no longer produce a worthwhile crop, so they allowed it to revert to grassland and kept it for grazing sheep. When the last war started, it was decided to plough up some of these downlands and local farmers dressed the land with the usual compound fertilisers. The first crops were disappointing. Then someone thought of applying minute quantities of copper, about two ounces an acre. The results were spectacular. Copper was evidently the catalyst that made the other fertiliser ingredients which the farmers had been applying, work. Trace elements of certain minerals are essential for plant growth, even though they may only be present in minute quantities. The copper once naturally present in these downlands had been exhausted by centuries of farming without replacement. Until the twentieth century, no one had realised that only copper was needed to make these once-fertile areas, prolific again.

Copper is a poison, but properly handled it is a vital ingredient in both crop and animal-food production. Its use has probably been instrumental in augmenting world food production more than any other substance, although it is not, of course, the only vital trace element. Copper deficiency affects many soils. The rich red sandstones which run north-eastwards across Britain look fertile enough but some areas are lethal to sheep, giving them a period of ill health called sway-back. It was then found that no more than a dusting of copper in a medicine would completely cure the sheep of this disease.

Before the end of February, my first lambs should be born. To me this really signifies the beginning of spring. I always feel this way, although I know that within ten or twelve weeks the first lambs will be in someone's oven and that their gambolling will be all too short.

I still lamb them down in the open, in sheltered fields, because I believe that they are better that way. But I do give them constant attention and have a barn fully stocked with pens and life-saving equipment for both ewes and lambs. Sheep are the most stupid creatures, especially at lambing. For instance they are so well insulated by their wool that they will not take shelter, and often drop their lambs in the most exposed places. The New Zealanders have a system of pre-lamb shearing, which in effect drives the ewes to shelter, but I have not yet dared to try it here. An exposed lambing will not hurt an only lamb, but 80 per cent of my ewes have multiple births and every now and then the second to be born will not get the ewe's attention, as she is too busy licking the first. If the twin lambs are strong they will usually get up and make sure the ewe notices them, but otherwise the family has to be picked up and taken inside.

I suppose some 10 per cent have to be brought in, as well as many of the triplets. A ewe has only two teats, and if she has three lambs, which many do, one of them will seldom thrive as well as the other two. Therefore I try to put the triplets to ewes that have singles, as I do any lambs whose mothers cannot rear them. This is not an easy job. Unlike a sow, a ewe knows her own lamb from birth, and will not willingly take a stranger. All sorts of tricks are used to persuade her to do so, a favourite one, if the ewe's own lamb has died, is to skin it and put the skin on the lamb to be adopted, but this is not always successful.

I have a line of adoption pens put up in a big barn. Here the ewe's head is held in a wooden yoke so that she cannot turn round; the lamb is then put loose in the pen with her so that it can suckle without the ewe being able to butt it away. After a day or two most of the lambs are accepted by their new mothers and the ewes can be turned out with their newly-adopted offspring. It is essential to return the lambs to the field as soon as possible, so that they have no time to pick up an infection indoors. Nor must they get softened by easy sheltered living or they will not be able to stand a bad day or two when they are turned out. In general, however, once a lamb is dried and has a stomach full of milk, it can stand anything.

But its stomach must be constantly filled up: it must suck very frequently until it is several weeks old which is the significant difference between the young lamb and the young calf. A newborn calf can survive a long time once it has had its first taste of colostrum milk. I once searched for a calf which I knew had been born the evening before and I failed to find it, nor did the cow seem to know where it was either. The field was alongside a main road so I thought the calf had been stolen. Two days later the calf walked out of a pile of straw in which it had hidden itself, and was absolutely all right.

The New Zealanders have developed a technique called easy-care lambing. They leave the ewes alone to lamb without help. Any ewe in trouble is marked down to be sold as soon as possible as clearly she is never going to be a good mother and rear future lambs properly. In this way they hope to weed out the problem ewes from their flocks and they claim excellent results, but then their lambing-success percentage is no more than 100 per cent while ours is around 160 per cent and our lambs are worth six times what theirs are.

I have learnt over the years that a lambing ewe should be given plenty of time, that she should not be helped unless it is really necessary. My wife always used to nag me about this, based on her own experience. One of our children was slightly overdue and I took my wife for a drive over a very bumpy road. So bumpy in fact that she insisted on getting out and walking, accusing me of having brought her there on purpose just to get the birth started. All females, she said, give birth in their own time; it is very stupid to try to hurry the process just to suit someone else's convenience. She was probably right.

Ewes about to lamb become quite tame and one can walk or drive among them without disturbing them at all. Once they have their lambs they revert to their old ways and bolt at the first sight of man or dog.

During lambing we shift the ewes every day round a sequence of small fields, sometimes twice a day. The ewes that have not lambed move out quite quickly and easily while those with lambs stay behind with them. Then we catch the day-old lambs, castrate and tail them and, if they are twins, number them so that we can join them up if lost. Castration seems to cause them little trouble at this early age; it must be done because after about three months they begin to think more of sex than of putting on flesh and there is an increasing danger that they will get their sisters in the family way. Tails are cut off for hygienic reasons; if they weren't they would harbour dung and blow-flies. We castrate with rubber rings slipped over the purse which cause it to drop off within a few days; we do the same for tailing. At a day old the lambs feel little discomfort and within an hour they are playing again. Years ago it would have been done at a month to six weeks, the purses cut with a knife and the tails shorn off with a hot iron.

Lambs' tails used to be a delicacy. Having one of the few flocks in the district, I used to be badgered by local villagers to let them have some tails. Their preparation was a mystery in itself and included being left on a stone floor for a week so that the wool would pull off easily. As an inducement one lady promised me a lambs'-tail pie which I duly took home. We heated it as instructed and I cut the crust. The smell was exactly that of a particularly sexy ram. I could not eat it and it did nothing for my wife, who gave it to the cat. But I still meet old ladies in Andover who ask if they can have some more tails. They must have done something for them.

After a couple of days, the ewes and lambs are usually well matched up so we move them to their grazing-fields, either on foot or by trailer. They still need a great deal of care, especially if the weather is bad and there is no grass. If feeding is necessary, we give them hay for a start and then when the lambs are about a week old, some compound nuts. The ewes love these nuts and chase after them as they are poured from the bag. Sometimes the lambs get separated from the ewes in the ensuing scamper which is a frequent cause of mis-mothering. It is essential to check the numbering and to see that all are matched up as soon as possible.

March

To give some idea of what my farm would look like in a typical year in March, I have drawn the endpaper map. In October I sowed Ashfield (85 acres) and Great Heath (60 acres) with winter wheat and Pill Heath Common (44 acres) with winter barley. In November I sowed Lower Cowdown (55 acres) with winter wheat and when I walk around my farm now, in March, I should be able to see these autumn-sown wheat and barley plants looking healthy and green, with the leaves beginning to lift above the ground. Back in October I decided upon my spring crops and if I haven't already got these sown, then I shall be in a fret until this is done. I should have managed to sow the northern part of Copse

Ground with 60 acres of spring oats in February and now I should be about to finish sowing 203 acres of spring barley in Cowdown, Brickhill, Reservoir Field, the southern section of Copse Ground, East End and Storey Heath. A hundred and twenty-two acres of grassland are in short-term grass leys waiting to return to cereal farming eventually in my crop-rotation system. In addition there are about 84 acres of unploughable pasture in Clay Copse, Little Meadow and Big Pond which are difficult to cultivate as they are steep and stony but all of them are regularly grazed by sheep.

It used to be said that March dust was worth a guinea an ounce as a seedbed and that the ideal time for sowing spring barley was midday on the fifteenth of the month. Like most sayings, it had only a fragile connection with reality. If your March soil is as fine and dusty as the saying implies, it is probably too dry to germinate the seed, however easy it may be to make the seedbed.

The fifteenth is a good day to sow barley, but it is no better than the fifteenth of January, February or April. It all depends on the state of the land at the time. I've had as good crops from January plantings as from March or even April. This last was in 1963 when, after one of the hardest winters on record, the land only thawed out enough to be worked on the fourteenth. As the soil had been frozen all winter there had been little leaching of natural nitrogen. A warm spring then encouraged the young barley to grow well and it sped through to harvest without any check at all. On the other hand, in some years barley sown in mid-March has met nothing but dry cold weather for a month or more, so the seed has germinated unevenly, with the result that by the first of May some of the plants are in the five- or six-leaf stage, while others are showing just above the surface. The effect of this very uneven ripening is a delayed harvest.

A late spring drought is most frustrating and it's as good a period to stay off the farm as any I know. There is nothing one can do about it unless there is irrigation available. So far very few grain crops in Britain are irrigated, except haphazardly by the Almighty. The best counter to a spring drought is a fine seedbed which holds moisture; one which is lumpy or chiselly is almost certain to dry out unevenly. Farmers on chalkland are better off in this respect for the chalk acts like a sponge, absorbing the winter rains and then slowly releasing the stored moisture to the crops as the weather gets warmer. The only time when chalky soil gives out is during a late summer drought, when the grain is far advanced towards maturity. Clays and other stronger soils don't act in this way. I have farmed both kinds of land and on balance know that there is nothing to beat a good chalk loam for cereal crops.

I wish I had more chalk loam on this farm, but I can't really complain because I had my chance. Nearly fifty years ago when I left my west Wiltshire tenancy, I could have taken a good chalk farm; I turned down several which were on offer at very low figures. But I chose Tangley simply because its grass, of which it consisted entirely in those days, was better than the natural grass on the chalkland. I was more interested in grazing cattle and sheep then than in growing cereal crops.

Nor was I the first person to have noticed how good the natural grasslands are around here. William Cobbett in his *Rural Rides* wrote about the 'excellent high meadows' of the north Hampshire hills. They are lush because they attract about ten inches more rainfall a year than the lower-lying lands around Winchester. The clay soil around here also grows very good cattle and sheep. I used to buy thin animals off the chalk farms. After a few weeks they would alter out of all recognition.

So I was not mistaken in eschewing chalk in those days, for there was more money in grassland generally. But those days may well be returning.

British farming fortunes are at the mercy of the Common Agricultural Policy and the overall interest of European farmers is towards livestock: the cow-keepers call the tune. Grain-growers are in a minority and so stand less chance of getting their way in the democratic, free-for-all, price-subsidy battles.

Most of the activity in Brussels is concerned with fixing next year's prices and the signs now are that grain-growers are going to receive less than the going rate of inflation for their crops. The very latest suggestion is that cereal prices should be allowed to fall gradually until they eventually match those of the United States of America. These are running at about 70 per cent of those fixed by the EEC. A drop of 30 per cent in the price of cereals would make life difficult for many of us, particularly those who have recently come into farming, and have borrowed a great deal of capital to do so.

The only way the average farmer can overcome this price-drop is to increase his production per acre and so reduce his unit costs and it is in the crucial month of March that we must get our tactics right.

At one time it was traditional to restrict the wheat plant's growth if there had been a mild winter and it was becoming too tall, or what we would call winter-proud. Such wheat used often to turn yellow towards the end of the month because over-rapid growth had exhausted soil nitrogen. What the crop actually needed was more nitrogen, and quickly. Instead, we used to run sheep on the fields to eat the wheat plant into the ground and inhibit growth. Some people still do this, but I have found that applying extra nitrogen and leaving the sheep on the grass is better for the wheat.

The use of nitrogen on wheat crops has increased enormously. Thirty years ago, the maximum application was 40 units or lbs an acre; today's forward-thinking farmers are pushing dressings up to between 120 and 160 units an acre. This does encourage very lush growth but it also brings with it the danger of excessively tall straw going down or lodging, which means that the whole crop falls into a tangled mess before harvest-time which materially reduces its yield. To counter this weakness, plant-breeders have produced newer and stiffer-strawed wheats which will stand up to high applications of nitrogen.

There have also been other developments. A wheat crop may fall down because the straw is too long and this problem even applies to a dwarf strain of wheat with a seemingly short straw. To stop this happening, the crop is sprayed with a growth-regulator which cuts straw growth by six inches or

more. So you have the nonsensical situation in which the more nitrogen you apply, the more the growth-regulator is needed so that the nitrogen cannot work on the straw but only benefits the grain. There is another snag: if there is a drought, or if anything else happens which restricts growth after the regulator has been applied, it actually harms the crop.

Yet further problems can occur: March weather can be very wild with winds and rain. Running over the crops with fertilisers, chemicals and growth-regulators can make an awful mess, even if tramlines have been left in the crop at sowing-time. If there is heavy rain, the machinery gets stuck; if there is wind the chemicals are blown all over the neighbours' land and this can do his crops or garden actual harm.

A helicopter or an aeroplane is the obvious answer and I have used both, but they are expensive and their use is restricted by bad weather, and by regulations on the number of hours a pilot is allowed to fly which, in Britain, must not exceed more than eighty hours a month. In New Zealand, the birthplace of aerial farming, a pilot's hours appear to be limited only by his endurance.

So the pressure in March is on to grow better crops than our neighbours. Not for us the doctrine of restricting output to market demand. Yield-increase is king, and farmers trumpet their record production, which is so humiliating to their less successful neighbours. Thirty years ago the average wheat yield here was a tonne an acre, now it is just over two and rising steadily. The best farmers claim three tonnes an acre and are aiming at four. I am sure an average of 2.5 tonnes is almost certain by 1985. Mind you very few crops are weighed in the fields, nor are field acreages absolutely accurate so how many achieve record high yields is not certain. Like fishermen's stories, farmers' yields are highly subjective.

But encouraging farmers to maximise their yield creates problems. For instance Britain needs to export something like four million tonnes of grain a year to make room for imports of an equivalent tonnage of maize and hard wheat which cannot be grown in our climate. Maize is used for starch and for making whisky, and hard wheats from North America are deemed essential for the manufacture of British machine-baked bread. Some of our barley is sold for malting to Europe but the bulk of our grain exports have to go to what are called Third World countries at the low world price for cereals. The difference between the world price and the EEC price is at the time of writing thirty-five to forty pounds a tonne and this subsidy is paid to all British wheat- and barley-growers, financed by a levy on imports of grain and by taxation.

At the moment this EEC levy is only paid on four million tonnes of British grain but as yields increase in the next few years it will probably be necessary to pay subsidies on another four million tonnes of wheat and probably on the same amount of barley which will soon be available for export. By 1985 this might mean a total of twelve million tonnes of grain, which at present world price-levels would cost the EEC nearly five hundred million pounds in export subsidies for British grain alone, or about fifty pounds per acre grown. Undoubtedly France, Germany and other EEC countries will also be having similar yield increases.

All EEC farmers are thus free of the constraints of ordinary economics. They are guaranteed a basic price for everything they grow, an open-ended commitment. Even if the grain fails to find an export market, the farmer gets paid, for funds are available to buy and store the grain, hence the notorious 'mountains'. How long can this policy be continued?

Many dedicated EEC supporters claim that the world price is fictitious, that the cost of the Common Agricultural Policy is an insurance against shortage. Nonsense. Except for a brief period between 1974 and 1975, when both grain and sugar were in deficit, there has always been a world price-level, 30 per cent to 50 per cent below that of the Common Market. The high prices of 1974 were caused by a grain shortage because the Russian harvest failed. The same held good in 1981. Russian sales are valuable because the Russians have vast resources of gold and other minerals which can be sold to offset the cost of all the grain they buy, so they do pay the actual price asked, whereas other importing countries all too often receive the grain as indirect aid of some kind. Only 15 per cent of the world trade in wheat for instance is really commercial. Thirty-five per cent of all world grain exports are taken by Russia, but should Russia learn how to grow her own food, and to handle and process it more efficiently, then she would be able to feed herself independently of the West, because the USSR possesses rich agricultural lands with enormous potential. If Russia was able to stop importing grain, it would decimate the world grain trade, which would mean crashing prices and financial disaster. This crisis could be close.

You may wonder if many farmers think of this when looking at their promising crops. A great many do. They cannot believe that the good times are going to last for ever and ever. That there will always be a bottomless purse to dispose of the surpluses that the ever-increasing technical efficiency of farming produces.

There are two obvious solutions. Every day we are told that some millions of mouths are born into this hungry world. Many of them doomed to a life of starvation and early death. All too true. But is there any reason why Western economies should be burdened with the cost of growing and transporting food to these hungry people who in any case can't pay for it? Would it not be better to encourage these countries to do the job for themselves? I have been to many of the world's hungry countries and they all contain within their borders sufficient resources, if handled correctly, to feed their existing and increasing populations.

To my mind Dr Norman Borlaug who works for CYMMIT, The Rockefeller Foundation research station in Mexico, is one of the greatest practical farmers I have ever met. He has concentrated on developing new strains of wheat, crossbred and selected from existing dwarf, short-strawed varieties, which flourish under tropical conditions. The results have been spectacular. In India the wheat crop doubled in a few years and the same principles, applied to other crops, have also pushed up yields. That many countries still do not manage to feed everyone is largely the fault of their economic and political systems. If they prefer to spend their incomes on armies and airlines instead of on food-production, it is not for us in these anti-imperialist days to tell them not to. That would be a return to the colonialism they used to complain about.

Some might call such policies immoral in the face of world hunger. But there is nothing immoral in restricting output to effective market demand in such products as silk stockings or motor cars. Why make such a song and dance about food?

Countries outside the EEC manage the problem rather better by imposing quotas or paying farmers not to grow wheat in the first place. These policies do not cost nearly so much as subsidising exports. In the United States the system is called the 'set-aside'. Every farmer sets aside, either voluntarily or compulsorily, an acreage of his wheat-land for which he is paid, but he must not grow anything else on it except grass for cattle. The legislation is still there and is likely to be invoked again if markets become depressed.

One of the first EEC Agricultural Commissioners, Sicco Mansholt, tried to initiate a similar policy in the Community which would have removed more than twelve million acres of land and turned it over to forestry or to recreational use. Unfortunately he was shouted down by the farming lobby. But it was the only sensible solution. Restrictive practices are condemned by almost every right-thinking person as being cruel because they seem to disregard the very real hunger and suffering in many of the developing countries. Perfectly true. But I don't believe these countries should be supported by charity for ever and ever which is the logical extension to over-production of food in the West. Of course there should be provision for extra supplies to cope with droughts and man-made disasters like wars, but quite a small store could be kept for these eventualities.

I am aware of all the problems connected with glut even, as I look over my growing crops in March and work out just how much nitrogen I should put on them and what chemicals to use, because I must get maximum output at present prices even though I know all the difficulties of disposal. It would be the height of folly for me to reduce my output in isolation, yet at the same time, I don't want to spend a penny more on fertilisers and spraying than I have to. The secret of successful farming is not following every rule in the book, or believing every adviser, but it is knowing what can be left undone without harm to the final result.

I don't very often grow oats for the very good reason that they are not one of the cereals guaranteed under the Common Agricultural Policy. There is of course a market for them in the horse-riding fraternity and for porridge. The acreage has been falling lately and I have grown a few each year to meet this trade and because oats make a good break from wheat and barley. That is, you can rotate them with these varieties. Fifty years ago of course they were a very important crop as horse-power was king on the farms, but they do have some drawbacks. They are particularly vulnerable to attacks by oat eelworm, a pest peculiar to oats, and to frit fly and can yield very irregularly. I once won a prize for the best field of oats in our district which were standing well; by harvest they had collapsed to the ground and I was quite ashamed of them. But you will have noticed that I am growing sixty acres of oats in part of Copse Ground. The reason is that the land is rather sour, deficient in lime, and oats are tolerant of this condition. I did not have the opportunity to apply lime last year so I am growing these oats and once the harvest is over I shall lime the field and plant it to winter wheat.

Oats also rather favour wet conditions and were very popular in Scotland where they were used to feed the horses and of course men. About a hundred years ago the mean Wiltshire farmers who had to give their men wheat or barley as part of their rations decided to try to make them live on oats instead. This did not work because there was no milk or butter freely available on English arable farms to eat with the oatmeal, without which it is not nutritious. The idea of living off what the land can produce is always an attractive one and many people are surprised I do not have hens clucking round my yard. I was a poultry-farmer once. Soon after the war ended I engaged a Canadian, whose husband was my bookkeeper, to look after a thousand laying hens. They were allowed to range about freely and I housed them in ex-ambulance-car bodies which we bought very cheaply and adapted. They paid reasonably well for a few years and then what might be called mass-produced poultry farming became the fashion with the birds crammed into battery cages. I was faced with following suit or giving up. Although I am as ruthless an exploiter of farm animals as anyone else, I just could not see myself living off caged poultry under these conditions and so when Mrs Jones retired I decided to stop keeping hens altogether, and to buy my eggs for breakfast. This coincided with my wife being ill and my having to cook for myself. Bought commercial eggs stuck to the shell and were often stale so I put up with them for a week and then persuaded one of my men to keep a few hens on my behalf if I provided the food. I now eat fresh eggs and don't notice the cost; they are much tastier.

Although modern battery cages revolt me I don't think the broiler houses give their victims the same treatment. My objections to broilers is that they are so cheap to produce that I am afraid they will kill the market for the pork and lamb that I produce.

By the middle of March, the bulk of my flock will have lambed. Many farmers rotate their sheep around their fields as the grass grows, but I believe that the grass that suits the sheep best is the stem that grew the night before, whilst she was asleep. If ewes are rotated then they are always being turned into pastures where the grass is beginning to get long and rather stale. Rotating also upsets both ewes and lambs. After a day or two in one field, they begin to look for the next move and become dissatisfied.

I set-stock my ewes at four, five or six to the acre, according to the quality of the grass. I like to have them all settled down in their individual fields where they will remain for a while, before the grass starts to grow, because each one lays claim to a little area of the field where she spends most of her time with her lambs; set-stocked in this fashion she will learn to make the best of what she has. Set-stocked, too, the ewes can be easily fed with extra compound if their field is a bit poor, without fear of them mis-mothering their lambs or losing them. I like looking round my flocks and watching the considerable variations between the various sheep; I soon get to recognise individuals and their idiosyncracies.

Ewes' milk is rich and as it is the vital factor in fattening the lambs, I do my very best to make sure that the ewes have plenty of milk, even if it means using expensive extra feed which could lower my profits.

I don't however give grain or compound to the lambs, even if there is very little grass for them to nibble at, for that would mean inefficiently converting cereals into meat: I expect to make my lamb-profits by turning grass into meat. Feeding cereal to lambs would be a mistake for it is nothing like as cost-effective as feeding the same concentrates to pigs or poultry. For instance, it takes about

3 lbs of feed to produce 1 lb of pork, but it takes between 5 lbs and 6 lbs of feed to produce 1 lb of lamb or beef.

On the other hand, there is nothing cheaper than spring grass converted into milk or meat and the earlier it is available the better. We could make more certain of good spring grass if we lambed rather later, say at the end of March, but this would mean a month's delay in the maturity of the lambs, which would, in normal times anyway, mean a rather lower ultimate selling-price. Grass loses some of its feed value by the second week in June, so after that the lambs take longer to fatten.

By the way, I almost forgot that fat is a proscribed substance these days. If our animals are too fat, the price is docked; the fat lamb which I was taught to aim for is no longer required. Or at least so I am told. The trouble is that if you want your lambs to do well, particularly on their mothers' milk, they form round fatty little carcasses when they are thriving, which look most attractive in the field. Lean lambs, which I've never yet managed to produce, are dreadful to look at.

French farmers seem rather more successful than me at producing lambs with very little fat on them; this they do by feeding them much more grain or compound feed than I would use. They don't of course have the easy early grass-growth that we do in England; they also seem to manage to obtain higher prices for their final product. Both the French and the Dutch have developed sheep which have largely fat-free carcasses, bred to depend on compounds after having been removed from their mothers early on and reared in separate farms on milk substitutes. The ewes' milk is then turned into cheeses, such as Roquefort. These breeds have been tried here, but they are late-maturing under our conditions.

I try to follow the needs of the market as well as I can. I used to cross my Mules with a Hampshire or Dorset Down ram which produced very quick-maturing, blocky lambs which seemed to run to fat. No one wished to buy them so now I cross my ewes with a Suffolk ram which is a bigger and longer sheep, a bit on the leggy side, but the lamb doesn't put on too much weight, although it does take longer to mature. Even so my single lambs are inclined to be a bit on the fat side for market perfection. Luckily the early spring buyers are not quite so fussy; they like a light lamb but will accept a bit of fat as long as it is not very old. My first lambs are usually no more than ten weeks old when I send them off and they are the best eating there is.

I am much more conscious of fat in my pigs. There has been enormous research into producing leaner pigs based on years of breeding and careful studies of feeding. Recently my pigs graded at the abattoir have been over 90 per cent in the top Q-grade which pleased me. My pigs are all sold for pork, and their grading is based on the depth of back fat, as it is with bacon. The fact that this can be accurately measured makes me much more conscious of it, because the price reduction when the measurement is exceeded is substantial. The reason why farmers have accepted these standards is that the majority of pigs,

71

about 90 per cent, are sold directly to the slaughter-houses while fewer than 10 per cent go through the markets. On the other hand 70 per cent of lambs go through the markets where grading is on the live animals. This is much less exact.

There is one further point. The pig's reproductive cycle is very much shorter than that of the sheep or beef animal; because of this higher fecundity, breeders have had more material to work on in a short space of time. Moreover a great deal more capital-enterprise and research has been applied to pig-farming than to beef and sheep.

The poor economics of sheep and beef production are distressingly obvious, as the following calculations show: a beef animal is probably at least two years old when it reaches maturity; a lamb takes rather less than half that time to reach the equivalent state, but a pig only takes six months, while a broiler chicken is ready in half that time. In terms of resources used to produce a kilo of liveweight gain, a beef animal will absorb between five and six kilos of grain equivalent; a lamb about the same, but a pig three kilos and a chicken less than two. This is a gross over-simplification because you can use grass to feed the ruminants – beef and sheep – but is a valid one.

It is therefore questionable whether, because of their inherently low productivity, either sheep or beef have much of a future in British lowland farming. Land to rent and buy is too costly. I purchased my land years ago and I keep sheep because I happen to like them, but my neighbours are not so fortunate for they face steep rent-rises every three years.

March 25th is quarter day when rents are due and some landlords are beginning to squeeze their tenants more than somewhat. Tenants can go to arbitration if they don't like the new rents but most fear that the verdict may go against them and they could end up having to pay more than they might have negotiated with the landlord in the first place. Hampshire land, rented at £2 an acre in 1945, now lets at £65 an acre. The price of wheat in those early days was £25 per tonne and is now just about £105. So, in less than forty years, rents have gone up thirty times while grain prices have increased no more than five times. Farmers have survived, or think that they have survived, because of higher productivity of men and machines and because yields have doubled on average, but it looks doubtful if they will be able to afford to play around with such low-productivity animals as sheep and beef for very much longer.

Even so tenants in Britain are not yet so hard pressed as they are in New Zealand dairying. There a young man with a herd of cows will pay the landowner 50 per cent of his total milk yield for the use of the farm for milk production. On an equivalent basis the sixty-five-pounds rent would be no more than 30 per cent of output which is comparatively cheap I suppose. But the New Zealander would employ no one but his wife and do most of the work himself. The Hampshire farmer will not be expecting to be in quite the same position.

April

Poets wax very sentimental about April, but it can bring the most diabolical weather. For instance, on the 26th in 1981 we suffered ten inches of snow. It was a Sunday morning, these things always happen on a Sunday, and the first we knew of it was a power-cut while it was still dark. Not to worry. Lambing was well over, and the lambs would stand a good deal of bad weather. The electric heaters in the sow-farrowing pens would be cut off but there was no frost and there should be no losses. I should have enough feed milled and mixed for a day or so, and we had bottled gas to cook the breakfast. Thus reassured, I turned over to sleep again. But there was something missing. Then I jumped out of bed.

Over the years I have dispensed with permanent fences as they are so expensive to build and to maintain and I have turned to electric ones. These are most efficient for two or three strands of thin wire can frustrate the most persistent escapers and they are easy to move about. My electric fences are powered with a very strong New Zealand energiser and until a few months before this I had been using car batteries to provide the current, but these had proved too much of a temptation for the local thieves to resist, so I had connected my fences to the mains. A power-cut would shut them off. By eight o'clock we had struggled through snowdrifts and over fallen trees to the nearest field. Something had told the sheep about the power-cut, and they had walked out in all directions, some 1,200 all told. The snow had stopped by that time, so we pulled the wires out of the drifts, re-erected the fences and connected a battery. But the sheep did not want to go back. They had tasted not only freedom, but also nice young plants of winter barley in the next field and were, as my foreman said, eating the hearts out of them. Once we had them contained they sulkily agreed to move back to some hay we had put before them. They spent quite a lot of time in succeeding days, even after the snow had gone, hanging about near the fence in hopes of another failure.

At the next field the sheep had had two hours' start, and were all over my neighbours' farms. Luckily they were all stockless farmers with no reason to get out of bed so they never saw the invasion. Not that the sheep would do any damage in that short time, but farmers are very sensitive about these things. As a protection I never complain if any one else's stock invades my farm, I know there will always be another day.

The power was not restored for three days; although we had the sheep under control, we had to haul water for the pigs and we could not use the feed-mill so we ran out of feed. Electricity is wonderfully convenient but if ever it is cut, we are in trouble, for we are woefully dependent upon it nowadays. If the supplies of power and diesel oil were to fail, for some reason such as a strike, the whole of British farming would stop dead. It would revert to the days when I started farming, when even the boss went to market by horse and trap. But now there are few horses and even fewer traps, let alone people who know how to harness and drive.

The snow came at an unfortunate moment, but then it is never welcome. I am all for those who enjoy their winter sports having fun, but I would sooner they went abroad to find their snow.

During April I inspect my sheep every few hours to make sure that the lambs are sucking well and that no ewes have died. There are many infections which they are heir to, some of which are viral and passed from one to another, others come from the grass; there are also deficiency diseases and maladies caused by their metabolism being upset.

The grazing habits of sheep are unusual. When I was a shepherd in New Zealand, I noticed that sheep liked their grass very short and very green. In New Zealand, most of the hill pastures were rough tussock but there were places where the herbage had been replaced by rather better grasses and I noticed that the sheep used to spend all their time in these little pockets, eating these down to the roots. I was told that these sheep-camps, as they were called, were the result of extra worm activity in the soil. No one then realised that the worms had followed the sheep to these camps because their dung produced higher fertility. The more dung, the more worms, the more fertile, the more grass, the more the sheep enjoyed eating it and so the patches grew larger. Nowadays pasture improvement can be much accelerated but the close-grazing principle still holds good.

When I returned to England, I discovered that this tight-grazing principle had been used on the Romney Marshes for centuries. I have read an account of it dated 1650 and the practice of keeping the grass short and the sheep so heavily stocked that they had to push their dung aside to graze was followed there until the area came under the plough about thirty years ago. I used to go to the Marsh quite frequently and in summer, after shearing, these heavily-stocked fields looked as if there had been a fall of snow.

The Romney Marshes were drained in Roman times; they have a very good alluvial soil of exceptionally high fertility. Compared with the Marsh, my land is of low basic fertility, but I can produce good growing conditions with nitrogen and I can match this growth with the sheeps' mouths. But I found that by farming crossbred ewes which are very good milkers and which will fatten two lambs in about twelve weeks, I had problems. Romney sheep are adapted to tight grazing on highly fertile soil; they are a big sheep but they have a low lambing percentage and the lambs themselves are very late maturing, and can stand these conditions.

If I put too much nitrogen on my pasture and so make it too rich, my crossbred ewes increase their production of milk and lambs to such an extent that it strains their metabolism and they come down with hypermagnesemia. The symptoms are abrupt and brutal. A ewe will be grazing with her lambs beside her one minute and lying down in a coma the next. Sometimes she will die instantly, at other times she may lie quivering for hours or even days while her lambs try to suck her empty udder. If a ewe is caught soon after an attack, it may be possible to effect a cure by injecting magnesium or calcium under the skin or into a vein, but this last is a difficult job. I once asked a doctor how he found the vein in his patient. 'By guess and by God,' he said. The only sure prevention against hypermagnesemia is either to feed the ewes a nut which contains magnesium during the period when they are most at risk, which is late March and early April, or to spread calcined magnesite on the fields. But I have found this latter method does not work at Tangley.

The malady used to be known as grass sickness and was particularly prevalent amongst hill sheep when they were brought down to lowland

75

pastures for the last lambing of their lives. The real cause has only recently been understood. It is now realised that bringing ewes from a bleak environment into a lush one forces them to over-increase their production of milk and lambs to a point which is more than their metabolism can stand.

When I had Welsh mountain ewes, I used to be driven mad by their habit of dying on me in April, particularly as they would often leave me with three-week-old lambs to look after. When I chose the Welsh breed, I knew that some would die each year, I had bargained on that; what I hadn't realised was what a nightmare endless dead sheep pose. I had been directed towards Welsh sheep by one of my mentors, to whom, as a boy, I had been sent to learn the way to farming success. He had certainly been successful, having been born in a workhouse and ended up with 6,000 acres. Any farm, he told me, should carry an extra Welsh ewe to the acre above ordinary stocking levels, to clear up the scraps, as it were, for they were so thrifty. He used to lose 30 per cent, but the remainder more than covered that loss and made a profit into the bargain. I found the ewes profitable, despite heavy losses, for they could be bought cheap and looked after their lambs well if they were alive to do so. But since I could not spray my land with calcined magnesite with any success and the Welsh ewes refused to eat artificial compounds and so declined to take magnesium in nut form, I became disillusioned by their mortality.

Instead I thought of having a flock of pure-bred ewes which had become acclimatised to richer lowland grass over generations and had adapted to the environment. But I could not find a pure-bred lowland-grass sheep in Britain which was as productive as the crossbreeds from the hills. Even if the ewe is bred pure she needs to be crossed with a meat-type ram to get the best results.

That it is possible over time to acclimatise animals to a richer environment, I knew from my own experience. When I went out to the Argentine fifty years ago, my old boss told me that the predecessors of the herds of cattle I was looking after had once roamed the dry pampas. Soon after the turn of the century, the natural pastures were changed to cultivated alfalfa or lucerne; this made many of the cattle blow or bloat which killed them. Over time the survivors came to accept alfalfa quite happily and eventually they passed this characteristic on to their offspring. It was a method of acclimatisation one could only afford when cattle were cheap.

I once thought of breeding from my own lambs for another generation so that my sheep would be increasingly familiar with their environment, instead of buying replacements every year. Moreover I thought that those who bred the sheep I buy in were taking me for a bit of a ride. So I kept some of my crossbred ewe lambs; they looked well but did not become as prolific as their dams. Moreover my shepherd did not like them so that really meant that I had no choice but to give up this idea.

Earlier on in my farming life, a very long time ago, I had had the notion of buying a farm in Wales for myself and breeding my own replacements there. Farms seemed easy to buy and the idea was attractive. But when I came to study the economics I found that it would be hard to make the Welsh farm pay unless I could improve the land and make it carry more sheep. I would have to pay the wages of a shepherd or of a local family to run the farm for me which would be expensive. Then there seemed little scope for land improvement as the soil was poor, much of it was too wet and drainage would be costly. It would also have been difficult to fence or improve areas of grazing which I would hold with rights in common with neighbouring farmers. Yet unless I raised the turnover sufficiently to pay for the extra investment needed and for the extra wages, it would not be a viable proposition. A Welsh farming family might have made a modest living from a few hundred ewes but then they would not be paying any wages. I enjoyed looking for the farm but decided in the end that Wales should remain in Welsh hands. Several of my friends did take the plunge and came out poorer in cash but richer in experience.

Although my April grass may look enticing and the sheep appear flourishing, I am always conscious that this emerald carpet can be lethal. Constant vigilance is essential and my shepherd tours the flocks several times a day, beginning at six a.m., in a Land-Rover. I use a different truck for bringing the sheep their food and they soon learn to recognise the engine-noise and associate it with their nuts. Otherwise it can cause problems if they keep following the Land-Rover around every few hours. Luckily they soon come to accept my presence and keep with their lambs. One morning I found twelve ewes down in one field with twenty-four lambs bleating unfed. Six were saved but the others died and they'd only been looked at two hours beforehand, which just underlines how essential frequent attention is.

Until about twenty-five years ago it was common, when going round the April pastures, to find some of the best, fattest, fittest lambs dead. Not poor starved little creatures but as many as 10 per cent of the pick of the flock. These lambs' stomachs would be found, on examination, to be full of wool, obviously sucked in by the lambs when seeking the teat. So every ewe, as she lambed, had the wool removed from around the udder. The lambs' condition was known as wool-balls and despite all our efforts they still kept dying. Further post-mortems indicated that their kidneys were soft and pulpy so we changed the name to pulpy kidney and a serum was eventually produced which reduced the incidence of the disease as long as we vaccinated each lamb at about ten days old. This was not only a nuisance and time-consuming, but it also knocked the lambs about and still the losses continued although not on quite the same scale. At last someone has come up with a composite serum which every ewe is now given shortly before lambing. It's not a 100 per cent effective but the incidence of death from pulpy kidney is smaller.

As though shepherds and farmers didn't have enough troubles of their own; other people add to them by letting their dogs stray. Sheep are particularly at risk from worrying dogs which drive the ewes into a corner while their lambs get left behind. Why do people let their dogs run wild in the country? A dog's nature is to chase game, and sheep are much easier to see and to catch than rabbits or hares. I have had some dreadful losses in the past, particularly from a combination of terriers and labradors, or pure-bred labradors. When the owners are found they cannot believe that their pets have been responsible, so I usually make them come and have a look at the carnage. Magistrates are much better at fining dog-owners these days, but the best solution is to shoot the dogs in the act.

Almost as frightening to the sheep as a dog is a hot-air balloon. Sheep don't mind noisy things, helicopters or planes but when one of these floating craft comes over they rush in all directions, especially when the heater blasts off. It's as if they imagined it to be some bird of prey, which by instinct they are trying to avoid.

Sheep get chased by dogs, panicked by air balloons, they pick up diseases from their surroundings, as well as from each other, they escape, they die; altogether they are tricky creatures to rear. But my pigs, I thought, would be very much easier. I kept them totally enclosed on about half an acre of concrete. It's long been known that pigs will fall like flies to any new strain of infection but that if kept in solitude they will build up an immunity to their own diseases. For ten years I have never brought a single live pig into my herd, any fresh blood comes from artificial insemination which is most efficient. Isolated from infection and from dogs, out of touch with the soil, how was it that my piglets were suddenly plagued with a form of scour which attacked them as soon as they were born? Losses began to mount, and no one knew what it was. Then my vet suggested that I send specimens to the animal-health laboratories run by the Ministry of Agriculture. This was not so easy as it sounded as the piglets were usually born on a Friday and the laboratories were closed for the weekend until Monday. However at last we managed to deliver some fresh specimens. The advice we received was a great surprise for the disease was one carried by sheep and the remedy was a vaccine called Lambivac which was luckily very cheap indeed to buy and easy to use. Farmers therefore have to beware of cross-infections between different kinds of animals, and of those between animals and humans.

One of the curses of dairy farming used to be contagious abortion caused by the infection brucellosis, which also affects man. I once lost two thirds of the calves of a dairy herd through what was called an abortion storm and my yields suffered accordingly. Brucellosis is now prevented by a slaughter policy coupled with vaccination and the UK is almost clear. Fifty years ago there was no vaccine or other prevention except the traditional remedy of running a billy-goat or a few geese with the herd. Both these animals were believed to eat the residues or cleansings after an animal had aborted which stopped the infection spreading. I tried the billy-goat but it certainly did not work for me.

Cows are also affected by the same excess of lush grass which gives sheep hypermagnesemia; with cows it is called milk fever. However cows are easier to handle than sheep, they are seen twice a day for milking and they do not die as speedily as ewes so it is possible to act quickly and cut down losses.

The first time I met this milk-fever disease in a cow was when I was a boy on a sheep-farm in New Zealand. We had a house-cow which I had to milk daily. One morning she was staggering about in the typical coma associated with this disease. I had never seen such behaviour in a cow before, nor had my boss. Should I, I asked, go and fetch the vet who lived over twenty miles away? 'Nonsense, my boy,' was the reply, 'vets cost money. Cut its throat and feed it to the dogs.'

There was a good deal more in that remark than an indifference to animal suffering. Vets were indeed expensive then and individual treatment for one animal was uneconomic, as it often is today. The great strides made in recent years are in preventive treatment of whole flocks and herds well in advance before the trouble starts. Nowadays I buy the necessary vaccine or serum and inject my animals myself. Vets make more of a living out of cat- and dog-lovers than they do out of farmers.

April is a very important month for those who make a living from grazing in summer cattle which they buy in from elsewhere and do not breed themselves. When I first left school, I became the farming pupil of a summer grazier on April 1st. My boss waited until the grass began to grow in April, then went out buying cattle. For the first month I attended markets all over south Shropshire with him, then helped him bring home the cattle he bought. There were no lorries in those days; we could either send the animals by rail to the nearest station which was within five or six miles of the farm, or we could walk them back. Anything up to fifteen miles was considered nothing but a good after-noon and evening walk.

Once home the young cattle were set in the fields on something like the same basis as I set-stock my sheep; that is the farmer estimated the carrying capacity of each field and filled it accordingly. I didn't know much about farming in those days but I could see that there could not be much money in the business for during April we bought about 800 heifers. Two months later we began selling them again. I have always had a good memory for animals and as I had spent hours following them home from the different markets, I knew many of them by sight. I noticed that some of them made even less when sold than they had cost. Greatly daring I pointed this out to the boss and received the reply that although the occasional animal made a loss, on average they showed a profit. 'How much profit?' I asked. 'Do you keep books?' 'Of course not, John. No proper farmer keeps accounts, we just do what we have always done on this farm.' 'But surely,' I said, 'a farmer should know what is what?' 'What I know,' he continued, 'is that I like grazing cattle and what I like usually pays me.' He was deceiving himself. What made the farm pay were the unglamorous lines like sheep, fruit and arable. The cattle were his hobby, and a very pleasant hobby they were. He used to delight in walking round them in the evenings, and got to know them all quite well.

It is possible to make some money out of summer grazing but for this the farmer has to live in market. Hanging over the rails watching the different lots being driven in. Every now and then the real expert will notice a bunch which is not making the right price, that can be bought just that much cheaper. And he buys at once. Or he may see that the trade is improving, and will send home for a load of his own to sell, kept ready for such an occasion.

Cattle, especially pure-bred beef-cattle, will fatten very well on spring and early summer grass, particularly in the grazing areas where the land is deeper than it is on the Hampshire hills. But the trouble is that everyone knows about this, and my boss was in competition with dozens of farmers all with the same idea.

Grazing cattle is, like most farming, a matter of arithmetic. But with the odds heavily against the farmer. They are very dear to buy in the spring and so is the price of finished beef. But then as increasing numbers come on the market, down goes the beef price. So the fattener has to put extra weight on the animals in order to compensate for this. Selling is a matter of very fine judgment because it is a race between weight and price.

After my early experience I never ventured into this field, but I used to keep quite a lot of cattle at one time. I had a large dairy herd and reared all the calves and also bought bunches of rather poor-looking store cattle to add to them. These used to be wintered on the downs, fed a little straw and would be sold in the spring to farmers, like my late boss, desperate to buy something to eat their grass. These did make me a little money, but only because I costed the winter grazing, and the straw, at nothing.

For ten years after my old boss died, I looked after his farm for his family. We still went in for cattle, but not for quick summer-fattening. Instead we bought good beef-type heifers in the autumn, wintered them well and then sold them to eager summer-grazing buyers in the spring. These cattle did show a margin of profit, but we never managed to earn enough to invest in the next autumn's supply without increasing the overdraft. The farm was made to pay, but only through growing cereals and keeping ewes and lambs.

The pattern of fattening beef animals is changing. Once traditional British joints of beef were from animals bred specifically for the job, they took two years to mature and were expensive to produce; they were fattened on rich midland pastures which had not been ploughed for centuries. But as costs have increased, farmers have ploughed up these lands which now produce some of the highest wheat yields in Britain. The Continental taste is for young bull-beef, intensively fed to be slaughtered at around twelve months; it needs longer, slower cooking than veal as it is slightly older but has neither the texture nor the flavour of good mature, old-fashioned British beef.

Farmers are changing their patterns and habits all the time, always looking for diversification so that they are not too dependent on the market; always trying to find new profitable ideas which will fit in with their soil and micro-climate. I frequently worry that I am too dependent on wheat and barley. I may have my sheep and pigs, but should I be trying out other crops rather than just cereals? Peas make a very good break from cereals and there is a guaranteed market for them as feed with an EEC subsidy, as well as a good sale for human consumption. Unfortunately they are a very tricky crop to grow; easy enough to plant, they often look very well, but their yields are very unreliable. Two years ago my peas were a success. As they were to be harvested dry, I left them until late, by which time they had caught some disease for which there was no cure and which turned them a nasty chocolate colour. I harvested them in the end, only to find that they were unfit for human consumption, but the guaranteed price was quite a good one. Then last year they came away really well. I made a beautiful seedbed for them about mid-April, and they grew on without a check. So good did they look that people came from far and wide to see them and photos were taken with me standing in their midst. The trouble was that they were all leaf and no pod, the yield was just half the last year's and they lost money into the bargain. No one could tell me why they failed except that everyone else's peas did badly last year too. They also did not seem to do much for an increase in yield for the following year's wheat crop, although according to all the experts, as they are nitrogenous, they should have done. In each case the yield after peas was the worst on the farm.

The advantage of peas is that they are sown later in the spring than barley, and this spreads the land-work. It also allows time for a really good seedbed to be made for them and gives the tractor-drivers something to do other than constant spraying.

Potatoes and sugar-beet are also alternative crops to cereals; their planting and cultivation would fit well into the average April. I have grown both, diversifying into potatoes especially in quite a big way. But the trouble is that my harsh flinty soils are not easy for a root to grow in; also clay soil is likely to set very hard. At 600 feet both crops mature rather late and sugar-beet in particular is difficult to harvest in a late autumn when it is wet. However, these crops could be grown here and be well mechanised so that they could be planted and harvested without the interference of human hands. But it was not always so. I was introduced to sugar-beet on my first farm the hard way. As a change from going to market the boss gave me a hoe and told me to single the beet. The beet seed is a collection of small seeds in a hard case and when they germinate they come up in a cluster of shoots. If they are not separated they grow together and like a stool of trees in a hedgerow will not grow the big single root required. Singling is a tedious and exacting job. The plants have to be carefully separated with the hoe-blade and all but one cut off. Then they have to be evenly spaced in the row about eight inches apart by cutting out the extra ones. If you make a bosh-shot you can wipe out the whole plant and this will leave a blank in the row. I always did the job standing up, but in Holland and France where enormous acreages are grown, men and women single them on their knees.

I never had a full day at singling beet as I was always being called away to do other jobs around the farm, but I was at it long enough to know that I would not do the job again from choice. The rows are terribly long and I used to have to crawl up them bent double so that I could see what my hoe-blade was doing. After singling, the beet had to be hoed at least twice more to correct any errors and then a third time to kill the weeds which grew round the actual plants. This last job was sometimes done with a horse-hoe, if the farmer had one. This was a wide metal frame with arrow-shaped hoe-blades which could be drawn up and down several rows at once by a horse. A boy led the horse and an experienced man held the handles and guided the hoe so that the blades always went between the rows.

On the bigger farms singling beet was paid at piece-work rates and the job was done by travelling gangs of workers who moved from farm to farm in a body. They were often Irishmen who travelled over to earn some extra cash; they camped in barns and would return later on to harvest both beet and potatoes. Many would come back to the same farm year after year, leaving their wives and families at home on their tiny holdings. They were grand workers, as emigrant Irishmen always are, but the gangs hardly ever come here now. Progress has displaced them. Beet seed is now produced so that each seed remains single and does not cluster. Modern spacing-drills avoid the need for singling, chemical sprays kill the weeds and the harvest is completely mechanised.

Mechanisation makes it very unlikely that I shall grow beet or potatoes here any more. Modern machinery can't cope with stones. They get picked up in the harvester, as they are roughly the same weight and shape as the potato, and it's an arduous job to separate them out later on. The housewife does not like seeing either stones or lumps of mud when she opens her bag of potatoes.

When I wish to impress a foreign visitor, I take him into one of my stonier fields and expect him to be very sorry for me. Americans in particular cannot understand why I should persist in farming among 'these rocks', as they call them. In their country, no one in his senses would cultivate such land, American farmers have left the stony, hilly lands of the eastern seaboard and have moved to the deep soils of the Middle West or the irrigated deserts of California and the south-west. This is the result of a farming system which pays the same price all over the country, making farmers concentrate on the best land and allowing the rest to revert to scrub and forest. They do not subsidise the farming of marginal land.

I was once picnicking with friends in the woods of Massachusetts and wandered off amongst the trees. Here I found the remains of a farmhouse and some Cotswold-type buildings with traces of cultivation and fencing. Similar evidence of abandoned farmsteads can be found all along the eastern seaboard of the United States.

If the Common Agricultural Policy were to be applied to all Europe in the same way as common prices are applied in the United States, huge areas of land, particularly in Britain, would turn out to be marginal and most of Europe's farms would be concentrated in France, the Low Countries and central Germany.

By the end of April all the stock, both cows and sheep, should be on grass, unless there has been a drought or a long-delayed spring. The possibility of being able to turn them out to graze so early is of recent origin, for pasture left to itself would not be growing yet, but during the last thirty years, better varieties and greater use of nitrogen have made this possible. Rye-grass in particular responds well to fertilisers, it is also highly productive.

Fifty years ago we tried to encourage the presence of rye-grass by overfeeding the cows with imported feeds and hoping that their rich dung would improve the pastures so that eventually the rye-grasses would take over from the other inferior species. Treading down the pastures all winter-long also helped to improve the grass. For, as in the New Zealand sheep camps I mentioned earlier on, tight grazing, increased dung, closer cropping all help to encourage better grazing. But it's a slow job to improve pastures in this fashion and takes several years before worthwhile results are visible.

Nowadays grasses are farmed and harvested just like grain and are quite a useful break-crop on an arable farm. By their use the spring has been advanced by up to six weeks. Instead of having to wait for grass until May Day or even later, cows, which require much longer grass than sheep, can be turned out to grass in early April and sometimes March.

When I kept cows this turn-out made a dramatic difference to the milk, output used to go up by 20 to 30 per cent and it all came from grass and not from purchased feed and expensively-made hay. Some farmers used to boast that their milk yield never rose when they turned their cows out to grass, inferring that they had managed their winter feeding so well that the change of feed made no difference. They must have been in the minority because the overall Milk Marketing Board's returns showed increases similar to mine countrywide. As a result prices fell and the surplus milk had to be made into butter and cheese, because the public does not increase its appetites by the season. But the profitability was undoubtedly there.

Until the coming of fertilisers most of the very early grass in this part of Hampshire and Wiltshire came from the water-meadows which had been set out along the banks of the Avon, Test and Kennet rivers in the chalkland. These water-meadows used to be flooded from about February onwards by means of a system of carriers and slip-streams from the main rivers. The purpose of flooding was not irrigation (there was always plenty of moisture), but warmth. All these rivers are fed by springs whose water has been stored in the chalk subsoil and bubbles up at a temperature of 45° F, sufficient to induce early grass growth. The water was led gently on to the meadows; once the soil had warmed up and the grass had begun to grow, then the water was drained off again. Tending these water-meadows was an art, and the man in charge, the drowner, was extremely important. There was tremendous competition between neighbouring drowners to be the first to have early grass for their masters' cows. The channels through which they led the water and drained it away again can still be seen in the meadows, but the system only works in a few places these days.

Drowning was another victim of the march of progress. Cheap fertilisers and new strains of grass allowed the dry lands to produce good early grass just as well as, and more reliably, than the water-meadows so many were allowed to fall into disuse or to become derelict. But the system left behind a wonderful network of streams and carriers along the chalk rivers where there is some of the finest trout-fishing in the world. I have no streams on my farm, but I am privileged to be able to enjoy fishing from some of them in the valley of the river Test which is only a few miles from home.

May

It used to be said that harvest yields could be foretold by the success of county cricketers in May. If several secured a thousand runs in the month, it meant that pitches were dry and hard, so crop yields would be light. But supremacy by the bowlers meant heavy crops, particularly barley, because this signified damp pitches with plenty of rain.

These days, though, few cricketers seem to be able to compile a thousand runs in May on pitches wet or dry, so this particular old wives' tale is no longer as accurate as it was. A much more certain measure is a rain gauge, because rain in May is absolutely crucial to growth. This applies not only to thin soils overlying rock or chalk, but also to those where there is considerable depth of soil. Farmers used to believe that May rainfall was essential to spring-sown barley but that autumn-sown crops, which were considered to be so deeply rooted that they gained their moisture from the subsoil, were less vulnerable. It is now certain, however, that drought in May and early June will severely reduce the yield potential of *all* cereal crops.

During late April 1981, I drove through the area south of the Salisbury to Blandford road and saw great level fields on chalk, bearing some remarkably good-looking crops of winter barley and wheat, dark green, thick and very lush. 'How foolish I was,' I told my wife, 'not to have bought a farm down here in the late 30s, then I could have crops like these, instead of the rather straggly ones I have at home.' Then came five weeks of drought beginning in early May. Crops were starved of moisture at a time when they were producing their flowering heads and wished to make maximum growth. When it came to harvest the yields in that chalk area were the worst for years; my own, while not particularly good, were about average, and were in direct relation to the depth of my soil: the deeper the soil, the better the yield. My crops had looked disappointing earlier on because the coldness of the clay had delayed growth until soil temperatures had risen.

Modern innovations in crop husbandry have exacerbated the effect of drought on yield, particularly of autumn-grown cereals. The lush growing crops we all strive for have been encouraged by heavy applications of nitrogen and any diseases which might reduce their leaf area are prevented by chemicals. For a successful harvest we need maximum growth. But I am now certain that such luxuriant vegetation exhausts much of the available water in the soil and the thicker the crop, the more will be lost. If the moisture is not replaced by rainfall, the grain will fail to develop because there will be no liquid rising up to the ear. This is particularly so where the land is shallow, and lies over chalk or rock. Although chalkland was once considered to be more moisture-retentive than other soils, that belief originated when crops were much thinner than they are today.

Some farmers have also suggested that the new varieties are no longer as deep-rooted as the original strains and that many fields suffer a plough-pan caused by the share as it drags along the furrow bottom, creating a seal through which the roots cannot penetrate in their search for moisture.

My own belief is that we are trying to grow heavier crops than the intrinsic quality of the land is capable of supporting. If we get a good rainy season, we get away with it, but when things go wrong, they go very wrong indeed. You only have to think about hydroponics, about the modern method of growing, say, greenhouse tomatoes in nutrient-enriched running water, to realise how much water plants need when they are receiving large quantities of extra chemical fertiliser.

However it is no good my thinking about irrigation at 600 feet. The cost of raising water to that height would be ruled right out of court, even for high-value vegetable crops. Irrigation has usually been considered uneconomic for cereals, but circumstances can alter cases. In some parts of France today, irrigation is being used on cereals in May as it has been found that the extra moisture at the end of the plant's development does increase the yield.

But while my crops may need rain, my grassland needs both rain and plenty of sunshine to make it grow. The ideal solution would be a thunderstorm every Saturday night followed by a long sunny period. By May my lambs are beginning to nibble grass, but they don't want too much of it. They should on no account have long grass for as it lengthens it loses some of the vital digestive factor which makes ewes produce milk and lambs produce meat. No one has yet been able accurately to measure this factor, but for centuries it has been known to exist. In my young days it used to be called the 'proof' in the grass, now it is called the grass's 'D-value', and it is at its peak in the middle of May, after which it gradually falls away. Its fall can be visibly measured by the declining milk-yield of a dairy herd at this time, a decline which it is almost impossible to reverse.

In spite of massive investments in costly research programmes on new varieties of grasses from all over the world and the experimental application of tonnes of fertilisers this D-value remains an indefinable quality, impossible to synthesise.

But super grass alone will not fatten my lambs. They need sun, and they will usually do better in a hot dry summer on little grass than they will in a lush one with overcast skies. They love the sunlight and it gives me great pleasure to see them stretched out asleep on a warm afternoon, growing bigger every minute. The secret is to keep them in full bloom. Bloom is rather hard to describe in sheep but in a horse, for instance, it shows when its skin literally shines. But once you understand sheep, bloom is just as recognisable. The lamb's coat seems to glow.

Intestinal worms will destroy this bloom extremely quickly and they are a real problem. The only certain way to avoid them is to use a completely clean field for the lambs every year, that is one which has been sown down the year before after a time in arable, or which has, for some reason, not been stocked with sheep. This is impossible for me to do under my crop-rotation system so the only answer is to pay close attention to my flock. My shepherd always looks around the sheep daily in May and I find it essential to see them for myself at least once or twice a week. This staggered inspection enables me to spot subtle changes in the lambs' state of health much more easily than if I saw them every day when slight changes are not so easily apparent. The most obvious symptom of any lamb problem is scouring, which suggests some potential digestive upset, a certain sign of worms. But by the time I have spotted this, it is almost too late for instant cure-action because the damage will have already been done. For two or three days before the conventional signs of worms appear, the lambs will have begun to lose their bloom. By the time I have physicked them, they will have already started to lose weight.

I sell my lambs by deadweight directly to a wholesaler which means I have to choose them by liveweight on the farm. The calculation is far from exact because a lamb's killing percentage is not an accurate calculation. A lamb in good condition, weighing, say, 70 lbs, will produce a carcass of 35 lbs. But if its condition is not so good, it will kill out at less than half its liveweight.

To find out if a lamb is in good condition or not, you put your hand flat on the lamb's loin, if it is firm and you can feel no hard bone, it is probably all right. Check that the tail or dock is about two inches across. Then run your finger from the tail to the rump and you should find a crack or indentation in the flesh. Put your hand on the lamb's shoulder-blades. If you can find them separately, he will do fine. But if the shoulder feels sharp, he is not yet really fit.

Drawing out lambs is a job many farmers leave to a dealer or a butcher, but I have always liked it to be under my control and have assessed hundreds in this way: I even tried to teach my sons. But they knew everything and would never listen to me, so I would let them make their own choice, send their pick to market where they would be graded live and then tell them to bring the rejects home and describe them to me. They learnt very quickly.

There are complications. I have been brought up to deal in pounds avoirdupois, but now I have to sell the lambs in kilos, which the wholesaler then sells on in pounds because metrication has been stopped by prime-ministerial order. It is a pity it cannot be reversed.

Farmers are always being accused of being bad marketeers, of not controlling the flow of production to the market more carefully. This is quite true, but it is not the farmer's fault. Lamb production is very seasonal. Weather conditions have, at least as much as anything I can do, to do with the time it takes the lamb to get fit.

The best single lambs born in late February should be ready for sale in May, at ten weeks old. In that time they should have increased in weight from about 8 lbs at birth, to between 70 and 80 lbs liveweight, all on grass and their mothers' milk. I never feed them any cereals. If I get my system right they will show better liveweight gains than pigs over that short period.

The spring lamb trade is a very delicate market, prices are at their peak around Easter, then fall away very fast as spring turns to summer. My aim is to get the maximum price per head as early in the season as possible which means balancing weight against price. For instance, say a 32-lb deadweight lamb is worth one pound per lb on May 12th, that is thirty-two pounds in all. If I keep the lamb another three weeks, it might kill out at 35 lbs, but by that time the price could have fallen by fivepence a lb which would make it worth, to me, £33.25. A profit of £1.25 certainly, but there are several other factors which have to be taken into consideration. By remaining on the farm, the lamb would be eating grass which could bring on other younger animals; its sale would have relieved, ever so slightly, the pressure on my grassland. Moreover if I had kept it on, it would have run into the period when the grass is losing its proof. Furthermore it would be increasingly at risk from intestinal worms which infest all heavily-stocked sheep pasture. These can be controlled by a good shepherd, which mine is, but the drugs used are expensive and, as with most medicines, never so effective as not incurring the problem in the first place.

These early lambs are like pears. They have to be sold when they are just ripe. If you put them by for two or three weeks, either they can get too big and too fat, or they can lose condition, then they have to be kept much longer before they are saleable. Marketing lambs is skilled work if I am to earn a few extra pence per pound, and as I sell nearly 2,000 lambs a year, every penny counts. I must supply the buyer with what he wants but the price he pays me is governed by the overall market which is highly competitive.

Up until 1980, the price of lamb was not controlled by any EEC regulations; the British farmer was however protected by a guaranteed price supported by a deficiency payment. This payment varied according to the market price; when this was low, some exporters found that they could undercut prices in France. For France had an efficient, but high-cost, sheep industry and Britain an equally efficient, low-cost one.

Under the Treaty of Rome, the founding fathers of the EEC laid down that all products should be competitive and free so it was permissible for Britain to undercut and export to France. The French however objected strongly. French farmers blocked roads, demonstrated outside buildings where their ministers were meeting and used all their political clout: they made their anger plain. The French government then introduced a levy system to bring the price of British imported lamb up to the French price. When this action failed to deter exporters, the French government declared an absolute ban on British lamb. To counter this, exporters started to send lambs to Belgium and Germany, which did not impose a ban, and from there, the sheep were sent into France.

These loopholes were vulnerable to direct action so the British government appealed to the European Court to declare the French ban illegal. The Court obliged on three occasions and told the French to desist. The French took absolutely no notice. I asked the then French Minister of Agriculture at the time, Monsieur Mehagnerie, how he felt about these judgments. He told me, 'They are of no concern to me. True, three have gone against me, but I am still in good health and spirits, and the sheep are still being kept out, and what is more important my farmers are still in business.'

As a result of the French lamb war, the EEC set up a new system which is financially so kind to us farmers that no one complains, but it costs the European taxpayer a great deal of money and it has effectively denied us export opportunity to the Continent for much of the year. Under this new system, the EEC fixes a price for British lamb on a seasonal basis; if the market price does not reach this level, a deficiency payment is provided to the farmer, financed from

Brussels. The French market therefore cannot be invaded when British prices are low because the deficiency payment acts as a tax on exports to other Common Market countries.

Under this new system, farmers receive the highest prices for their lambs that they have ever had, and the housewife, in times of plenty, can buy the cheapest lamb in Europe from farmers protected by this deficiency payment. However she, or her husband, pays in the end because the farmers' money comes from Brussels, which comes in the first place from the British taxpayer and consumer.

Spring is no time for relaxation on any farm, for after the lambs and the sheep have been looked after, silage must be made and weeds in the crops have to be sprayed. In May the pressure is on to make sure of next winter's fodder. It is too early for hay but everyone with any stock is deep in the throes of making silage. Everyone except myself, because I have no cattle now and sheep do not take kindly to silage. Nor do I take kindly to silage-making as it is now practised.

At one time silage was thought to be a useful alternative food to hay and a way of conserving grass in a bad season. The process was simplicity itself and consisted of cutting and carting green grass to clamps or pits in the fields, rolling it well down, covering it with earth so that the air could not reach it and leaving it alone until winter. Then all that had to be done was to uncover the pit and either haul the grass out, or let the animals help themselves.

I made thousands of tonnes of this stuff and it was just rather grudgingly eaten by hungry cows. It stank to high heaven and anyone associated with it stank too with a particularly clinging smell. So much so that one cowman I knew complained to his boss that his wife would not let him into bed during silage-feeding time, which lasted all winter. 'Well,' said the boss, 'get your wife to roll in it then she won't notice you. My wife doesn't object to me.' On hearing this, the cowman's wife went to the boss and said, 'Your wife can't afford to be particular, but I am still young and can pick and choose.'

All that could be said for old-fashioned silage was that it was better than bad mouldy hay, but not very much. To begin with, it was too wet and cows used to have to eat enormous quantities in order to absorb sufficient dry matter for survival. It was indigestible and variable in quality, particularly if the farmer had delayed making it until late in the season, after his hay crop had failed. To make nutritious silage, it was finally realised, was a highly skilled operation – so skilled in fact that whole books have been written about it and specialist college courses try to drive the lessons in. Grass for silage can be cut earlier than that for hay, the earlier the better for then it has a higher D-value. Although no one really knows what D-value is, various figures are recited over BBC Radio 4 every morning at six ten a.m. when all keen farmers should be listening to market reports. But the earlier the grass is cut, the smaller the bulk, so, as with selling lambs, the day to begin silage-making is a matter of fine judgment. Basically grass silage should have a high dry-matter content, it should not be ensiled at more than 25 per cent moisture which means it has to be nearly as dry as hay, which should be less than 20 per cent moist. So after silage has been cut, it should lie for a day or two and be allowed to wilt before it is stored in big clamps. This, in our climate, is a tall order, for obviously it will only wilt if it is not raining. Most farmers ensile their grass fields at least once and then graze the regrowth. If the fields are cut early enough in May, there would even be a chance afterwards for a further crop to be planted such as kale or roots.

The best feed is well-made hay but making silage is a great deal easier. The whole process is well mechanised nowadays, but the machinery is very expensive for the small farmer to buy, so some have to rely on hiring in contractors to cut their silage. But a contractor can never be certain that he will be free to come on the day requested. With D-values falling daily, a good deal of frustration is suffered all round.

Because of the difficulties of handling silage, I have not made any lately, but I know about the new developments that have taken place. One is to cut the grass, let it wilt in the normal way and then to bale it up with a baler and immediately put it into large plastic bags weighing fifteen hundredweight each. These bags are then sealed in order to stop fermentation and spoiling. This method is particularly useful if you only want to make small quantities of silage or if you wish to feed your animals out in the fields – provided that is, you have a loader which can lift the bags.

It is perfectly feasible to make silage later in the season with much more mature herbage. Indeed it is much simpler to do so but the D-value is not so good. A few years ago there was a craze for maize silage but for this the cobs, or seed-heads, need to be fully formed and ripe which is not easy to accomplish under cloudy British summer skies, except very occasionally.

Maize growing is all a matter of latitude. In Brittany, for example, only two hundred miles south of my farm, maize silage is the main support of the dairying industry and very efficient it is too. To learn what good farmers the French are is always a shattering blow to the average British agriculturalist for he has been brought up to believe that all European farming takes place on antiquated peasant holdings where a couple of cows are tethered on some rough heathland; he thinks that his own much larger-scale and highly competitive enterprises will wipe such antediluvian systems off the map. It is however extremely important to remember that the French have at all times considerable advantages over us which they do not hesitate to use. They have a warmer climate, in Normandy and Brittany, where most of the cows are kept; it is milder even than in Devon and Cornwall and the grass grows for eight or nine months of the year; farms are small and rarely employ hired labour so they can undercut any farmer who pays wages; and perhaps most important of all, because of their small scale, there are many more of these farmers and they have considerable political clout. Politicians are going to listen far more attentively to ten men with twenty cows each than to one man with two hundred.

Still, at the moment, we British farmers are managing to get along pretty well

91

and there is no doubt that when it comes to such activities as spraying the land with hormone weed-killer, then our larger units make it easy to use the latest modern machinery. May is the month for attacking docks, charlock and wild oats, all persistent weeds which do great damage to crops if allowed to grow and seed.

There was a time when this farm was known as 'Tangley Docks' and rumour had it that gullible Andoverians were sent for bicycle rides to see the ships here. The name came from the profusion of docks which used to infest these fields, their great brown heads waving above the crops by harvest time. Docks have deep tough roots which are difficult to pull out of the ground: my old foreman told me that his father had once taken a dock root home which was as big as a parsnip. He had carved it into a pipe and smoked it for three years and then, breaking it, he had thrown it out into the garden, where it had rooted once more. There are few docks now for they soon fell victim to the first hormone weed-killer.

But there are still wild oats. A wonderfully beautiful plant – so the flower arrangers tell me – but ruinous in a field of grain. Wild oats usually ripen before the main crop and the seed drops out to re-infest the field. You can see wild oats dancing over wheat and barley just before harvest. One dose of weed-killer is not enough for the seeds germinate irregularly, some lying in the soil for several years before showing themselves. I have seen them come in a field which had been free for a dozen years. There was a time when there were no wild oats here, for the land when I came had been in grass for about twenty years. The oats came in amongst some wheat seed which I had bought from East Anglia and although the wild oats are under control now, it will take more than my lifetime to get rid of them altogether.

Their persistence in the ground does not match that of the crucifera weeds of which the worst is yellow charlock. At the outbreak of the last war a friend of mine ploughed a field which had been in grass for at least a hundred years. It came up covered with charlock. I put in a water-supply some years ago and the trench I dug grew thick with thistles, charlock and docks. Obviously one of my predecessors had ploughed very deep one year in the hope of burying his problems.

Few farmers under middle age can remember what losses we suffered from these common weeds. You could have a splendid strike of a new crop of spring barley at the end of April and by early May the soil between the plants would show a sprinkling of tiny charlock seedings. There was nothing to be done to get rid of them. When labour was cheap they could be hoed or pulled out, otherwise they were just left to grow and within a few weeks would dominate the barley. To lose half the crop one year was bad enough but, like wild oats, charlock ripened before the grain and infested the land for another generation, so you might well lose even more the following year. I have been using weed-killers methodically for the last thirty-odd years but charlock still appears. Not so thick as it used to, and probably no longer affecting my yield, but if it were allowed to seed I should be in trouble for many years to come.

Charlock can be controlled by chemicals but I have found that its disappearance encouraged the growth of other weeds which until then had been no problem at all. One of these is chickweed which does not fall victim to the same chemical as charlock. There are other weeds too, such as poppies and cleavers – goose grass – which have been lurking in the hedgerows or growing unnoticed in the fields but which have been suppressed or overshadowed by the dominant charlock. These other weeds are not always susceptible to hormone sprays and need newer, more sophisticated, more expensive chemicals to control them.

The basic chemicals used in the manufacture of weed-killers are few but the firms supplying them have given each of their own products individual brand-names instead of restricting themselves to the name for the scientific base of the product: this is most puzzling for the farmer. As farmers have rarely had a scientific education, they are unable to do more than read the labels on the weed-killer containers, so confusion reigns as to which chemical is best and which is the cheapest to buy to make an effective job. I make it a firm rule to avoid chemical salesmen at all costs and I never read their advertising material. I make my choice as to what to buy on the basis of talking to friends and members of my family and pooling experience. I grew up in a period when the way to farming bankruptcy was to spend money and I never do so without deep thought. If I do engage in a new investment I pay a great many visits to other farms and take much advice before committing myself. A good motto when considering farming expenditure is 'When in doubt spend nowt'.

Learning about improvements from the successful example of other farmers is extremely important. I have travelled thousands of miles looking at farms in this country, in Europe, Asia, North and South America, Australia and New Zealand, and have learnt a colossal amount in the process. Not all systems are strictly comparable for climates vary, but the basic principles of farming are the same, and farmers everywhere are always willing to talk and to show you what they are doing.

English farming has never been really innovative. Our modern dairying successes have been built on the Dutch use of grassland, which is the best in western Europe, and on the Friesian cow which was re-introduced from Holland soon after the last war, until nearly 90 per cent of British dairy herds were black and white. But now, regrettably in many eyes, they are being subtly changed by the infiltration of the Holstein.

The Holstein is the heaviest milking-cow in the world and is a derivative of the Friesian which has been specially developed in North America to make the best use of what could be called dry feed as against grass and grass silage. The Holstein is one of the biggest breeds of cattle there is, with a huge stomach for efficient digestion and a powerful frame to carry it all. The theory is that the more grain that can be crammed into it, the more milk it will produce and so for countries where grain is cheap it is first class. The trouble is that it does not

93

flesh up very well and has very poor beef conformation; it is best in hamburgers. But as milk pays better than beef, farmers cannot be blamed for preferring the Holstein to the Friesian, which although a good milker and quite a good beef animal is not able to produce the quantity of the Holstein.

English farmers have also gained many ideas on pig-raising from the Continent. About thirty years ago we started importing Danish Landrace pigs, against the wishes of the Danes, I might add. (These pigs had come through Sweden to which they had been smuggled in the first place.) But even more significant was our adoption of the Danish system of testing and breeding stock for litter-size and performance. The application of these techniques has made our pigs some of the most efficient producers of pork and bacon in the world.

The poultry industry, both for eggs and meat, is now based entirely on American hybridisation techniques which were initially viciously opposed by established interests, as were the importations of the Continental cattle which now dominate the beef trade. In all but one of the last twelve years the supreme championship at the Smithfield Show has been won by a crossbred of one of the imported breeds.

Arable farming has also been dependent on the Continent. Rather more than half the seed-grain we use originates from there. Grass seeds are now coming from Holland and many of our techniques of fungicide control and fertilising began in Belgium and north Germany.

These innovations have not come here through aggressive Continental salesmanship, but because inquisitive British farmers and traders have taken the trouble to go overseas to see what is new and successful, and then have returned home to try to adapt to their own farms what they believe to be the best of the European notions.

The reason that we have proved so adept at pinching other people's ideas, although that hardly describes the taking of advice so freely given, has been historical. Every other country in Europe protected its farmers against imports and supported them with higher prices except Britain, which was the odd-man-out in Europe, exposing its farmers to the free importation of food from all over the world. Against such competition, British farmers could ill afford to take risks with innovations which might add to costs without increasing returns, so we all took a very good look at what our neighbours were doing, let them make the mistakes and then built on what was successful. It has certainly paid off. Only since joining the Common Market have our farm prices approached European levels.

June

When I milked cows here, yields always began to fall around the first week of June. This coincided with wheat coming into ear. Grasses too would push up their seed-heads and it seemed that the vigour of spring in all the crops was leaving the leaves and going into the seed.

This nutritional vigour is impossible to reproduce later in the year, even with the most extravagant fertilising. You can grow a very lush-looking field of grass in late June but it will not yield the milk it would have done a month ago. Both cows and sheep now need more grass, yet produce less milk and meat. So by the middle of June I am trying to grow this extra for them and I am now leaving it a little taller in the field. For instance, in a good growing May, I am quite happy if I throw a tenpenny piece for twenty yards and can still see it on the surface. Now I like to see it from about five yards.

I still try to graze hard enough to prevent the actual seed-heads from showing but this is getting increasingly difficult. The grass-plant is determined to make seeds. Even if the seed-shoot is kept very short by grazing, it will still make a seed-head at an inch long. In an attempt to stop this happening on Romney Marsh, at one time, it was cut with gang-mowers so that it looked like a lawn. I never tried to do this here because my flints would have destroyed any steel coming in contact with them. As a gang-mower is just like the old-fashioned lawn-mower, but pulled by a tractor, the blades would have had all the impact of an irresistible force on an immoveable object had they been driven into one of my flints. A pushed lawn-mower is much more yielding.

Instead of mowing, one of the traditional ways of keeping grazing short is to run cattle with the sheep, and when I had my dairy herd this is what I did. I didn't run the milkers with the sheep but the young heifers which were waiting to come into their first oestrus. The life of a dairy cow in the herd is about three lactations, so I always needed to renew one third of my herd with new heifers every year. In this case, as with pigs, it certainly paid to rear my own. I knew their breeding, and if my own herd was free from disease, they kept that way. Any lack of profits could be set against the general cost of maintaining a dairy herd.

But now I no longer have dairy cows, or heifers, nor do I ranch cattle. The basic theory behind beef-cattle fattening is that you buy them for, say, £300 a head in the spring or previous autumn, fatten them up and sell them when the grass is losing its bite for, say £400. You have a hundred pounds therefore out of which to finance your profit and any overheads you may have incurred. The trouble is that they may cost a good deal of money to buy initially and then when you come to sell them, their price is usually falling, because everyone else is doing likewise, so there is nothing certain about any of this and you may have to sell them for less than they cost in the first place.

It was different in the 30s when land could be rented for fifty pence an acre or even less. Then I did ranch cattle bought very cheaply, for I could look after them myself as this only entailed a cursory visit two or three times a week. I used to buy and sell the bunches when they showed a small profit. My ambition was to build up my acreage to 2,000, when, I hoped, I would be able to make a living by ranching in this way. But before I could increase my acreage and improve the type of cattle I was buying, the war came. I had to plough up my land, drop my ambition and become a 'proper' farmer. Although this enabled me to become a capitalist, it altered the economic constraints on my farming to such an extent that I cannot afford to ranch the land I now have, much as I would like to.

I do however have neighbours who keep some good beef-cattle, six or seven hundred head. They started, as I did, with odd lots of cattle but are obviously doing well enough now to buy much better ones. So much so, that when a visitor says to me 'I saw some nice cattle on the way to your farm', I don't like to correct him, I just smile and take a little of the credit. I asked my neighbours if their cattle paid, 'They don't exactly pay,' they said, 'but they do keep their value in these inflationary times.' Rather better than krugerrands I suppose. You can at least eat them.

There is no doubt that beef-cattle are easy to farm and look most attractive on a June evening when they are grazing some lush pasture. Mature cattle seldom get ill and as long as their owner has enough cash to finance them and very low overheads, he can enjoy them to the full. It is because they are so free from problems that there is always such a demand for them, and so they are dear to buy. More a hobby than a business, really.

They would need better fencing than the two strands of electrified plain wire which I use for my sheep and they would no longer fit in with the rest of my present system so although I sometimes wish I could now fulfil my old ambition, I am quite glad I no longer ranch. The cattle might not prove profitable but I suppose they would help to keep the grass from going to seed so quickly.

The wheat is also coming into seed in June so it is almost too late to spray for fungus diseases but a sharp watch has to be kept for aphids which are apt to show up on the wheat towards the end of the month. I had never seen one of these until about five years ago and then a field of wheat became covered with these horrible little green monsters. They start on the underside of the leaves and then rapidly overwhelm the whole plant. The rule is that if there are more than five on an ear they should be sprayed. They suck the sap from the plant thus causing the grain to shrivel. Their reproductive energies are fantastic. Half a dozen on a plant will multiply daily. As the spraying tractor brushes the crops it gets covered with them and literally bucketfuls could be collected if they were any good for anything. In extreme cases they reduce yields to negligible amounts. I was on a farm in France once where they were threshing wheat sheaves, and getting practically no grain at all. I asked why and they said it was *la mouche* for which at that time there was no cure.

Aphids have been known for a long time to attack roses and fruit trees, but have given little trouble to cereal crops until recent years. There was a theory that they came from the Continent. Pilots of light aircraft claimed to have seen them flying across the Channel. As this particular rumour emanated from an aerial-spraying firm there was some suspicion that it might have had a basis of self-interest. I believe the root cause is continuous wheat-growing which is common in many parts of the country now. It allows a build-up of suitable food for aphids, and other pests, which then winter in the plant residues. The aphid is infinitely adaptable, the young are born pregnant in spring and summer, but as eggs in the autumn, in which form they can survive the winter.

Aphids are also vectors for a variety of cereal diseases, notably net blotch in barley. The culprit is the bird-cherry aphid which is found in autumn on the leaves of the young wheat from which it transfers to the barley in the early spring. Why the Lord ever invented aphids in the first place I can't tell, but they must have a function if it's only to warn us of the dangers of over-production and bad husbandry.

The effect of aphids and fungus diseases is to destroy the leaves of the cereal plants so that they can no longer feed the main stem, and so swell the grain. The leaves of all plants curl up and die as maturity approaches, but premature dying reduces yield.

If, after conscientious spraying for all known diseases, the ear still seems undersized, then there was probably too little rain earlier on so that insufficient moisture was available to swell the ear at the crucial moment. I am re-inforced in this belief after studying the results of the crops in the Beauce area of central France, just south of Chartres, where there is some of the best arable land in Europe. Although the crops there always look much better than ours do, they never seem to achieve commensurate yields which is not surprising when you think how hot it is there early in summer whilst we have a further month's milder damper weather left. All the same, if I had my time over again, I would like to have farmed in the Beauce. I first saw this great open country, just crying out for mechanisation, soon after the war. I wish I had bought a farm there then, for there were no rules against so doing in those days. Had I done so, I would now be getting all those extra aids which the French farmer receives. During 1981–2, the French government handed out nearly a billion pounds to its farmers. The first slice was to ensure the re-election of President Giscard and now the new President, Mitterand, is doing his best to emulate his predecessor by increasing the amount.

Another Gallic way of helping farmers is to shield them from high interest rates. The largest bank in France, Crédit Agricole is, at the time of writing, lending money at rates varying from 5 to 10 per cent, the lower rate being for young farmers, under thirty-six years old. I was changing money the other day at a country branch of Crédit Agricole, and asked if I could borrow £50,000, secured on my farm in Hampshire. Not a hope I was told. You have to be an approved French farmer.

It is obviously unfair that a French farmer should be able to borrow money to put up a new cowshed at half the cost to his British competitor. It is even more unfair when an Italian horticulturist can borrow at between 1 and 3 per cent over thirty years to put himself in a commanding position in trade. We are not however the only sufferers. In Brittany there is a very good co-operative selling vegetables, particularly cauliflowers and artichokes. They used to have a very good trade with the Nordic countries which they lost. On investigation, they found that Italian freight costs were so subsidised that the Italians could land their goods in Stockholm for less than it cost the Bretons to pack their produce.

I believe these distortions, and others too numerous to mention, will eventually destroy the Common Agricultural Policy as we have known it, or at least as it was laid down. The political cost of putting whole populations out of business, which is what a free-for-all would entail, is more than national governments could face. Only in Britain, where farmers are in such a minority, can governments afford to disregard them. It is sensible to expect that far from withering away, national aids will proliferate elsewhere as each country protects sections of its own farmers from disaster. This is particularly so in the present industrial recession, where the only alternative to small farming is the dole queue.

The problem will be aggravated when Spain and Portugal join the Community. Expected competition from Spanish wine and fruit is already feared in France and Italy. What is not yet understood, is how competitive Spain may turn out to be with her ordinary arable crops such as sugar, grain and oil seeds. Concern has been expressed about the cost of supporting surplus olive oil, but the alternatives to olive oil are even more frightening. In a small area around Seville I was shown a quarter of a million acres of land which had been transformed from olive trees into ordinary dry-land farming, growing wheat, sugar-beet and oil seeds. Some of the sugar-beet yields under irrigation were as high as anywhere in Europe, and sugar-cane can be grown right alongside as well. There is an overall shortage of water for irrigation at present but I was told there was plenty of scope for greater development of existing resources.

All this is going to add to the problems of financing the Common Agricultural Policy, which I am sure will eventually change to a much looser system within a common tariff, but with each government and its farmers paying directly for the cost of their own support.

I usually try to have a holiday in June, but it is one with a real purpose, to get away from haymaking. If I am at home at this time, my foreman says he is due for a break, and leaves me the job I most dislike, so I try to work it the other way round. Haymaking used not to be the nightmare it is now. In simpler days, I used to start cutting after the longest day, leave the grass to dry out in the field for a few days, perhaps toss it about with a tedder or other machine, and then sweep it into a stack which was thatched until the winter. There was quite literally nothing to go wrong. If I was very stupid and started to stack it too soon before the sap was out of the grass, the hay used to get hot, even charred, but I never had a stack catch fire. If the hay was wet it used to go a little mouldy, but the fact that one put it in a large rick meant that it all heated up a bit and so cured itself.

In my young days the sweeps, like giant wooden toasting-forks, were drawn by two horses. These were eventually replaced by a tractor. Tractors are much stronger than horses, and the hay, especially when it was a bit damp, was often tangled into horrible lumps which were difficult to tease out before they were swung up on the elevator on to the stack. Then someone invented a machine which threw the whole sweep-load on to the stack, leaving it to the poor building-crew to tease out the lumps. A hard job.

About 1930 a rural genius, Arthur Hosier, devised a very lightly-built sweep which could be fitted to the front of one of the many excellent large old cars which were then on the market for about five or ten pounds. These car-sweeps were much faster than horses or tractors and brought in light loads of hay which were easy to disentangle. I made thousands of acres of quite good hay with them.

After that progress raised its ugly head. Hay in a stack was always difficult to get to the animals, for it had to be cut and baled, or loaded loose on to a cart and then trundled to manger or field. So some bright spark in America invented a baler which would packet the hay on the field in handy sizes, weighing about 50 lbs, just right for feeding out later. I had one of the first of these balers and have never made good hay since. A small bale is not big enough to cure the hay in, and unless it is made of superlatively dry material it will go mouldy. Picking up and handling the bales, although quite well mechanised, is a long and tedious job. The balers themselves are very temperamental, and will play up at the drop of a hat. These machines were invented in California, where it never rains in the summer and it is possible to make good hay all the time. In fact it is often so dry that the leaf drops off and they bale at night when it is a little damp. I have never known it like that here.

A neighbour retired some years ago and at his sale were two old sweeps and a stacker. I bought them for a few quid and told my old foreman that we were going to make hay in the old-fashioned way with sweeps and a stacker. He refused point-blank. To regress like that would make us the laughing-stock of the district, he said. I weakly gave in, and have regretted it ever since.

The best hay according to the nutritionists is that cut well before the longest day, June 21st. After that it gets seedy and is nothing like so good for the stock. This may well be true, but early hay is very tricky to make. The grass is soft and full of nature, and the bales will heat and twist themselves into all sorts of shapes. If they are stacked they will often fall down, even in a barn with solid walls.

I should add that I don't usually plan to make hay but there are times when I have a surplus of grass for which I have no other use. It is difficult to estimate grass growth with any accuracy and once I have an excess it is better preserved as hay than allowed to go to waste. I normally prefer to buy most of the hay I need from one of my neighbours who has made too much and who will sell it to me for about fifty pounds a tonne. I am then the master of this situation. I can pick and choose, and am not landed with the results of my own lack of skill.

Another June task which I do not relish and for which I no longer have the knack is sheep-shearing. I can do it, but now prefer to employ others.

During the 1920s I went out to New Zealand and there I learnt to shear. It

100

came about this way. The shearing gang on the farm where I worked, was having its Sunday rest and one of them began to bait me, squaring up to me in best boxing fashion. I had retired from boxing years before so I picked up a pair of hand-shears with eight-inch blades and pointed them at him. He must have thought I meant action for he backed off, grabbed his horse and rode away. He did not re-appear, so the next morning the boss said that as I had chased him away, I had best take his place. The first sheep I sheared was a dead one which had succumbed in the night. Its fleece was still valuable however and it was useful for me to practise on. During the laborious struggle that followed, I managed to cut its throat.

I never actually killed a sheep while shearing but I certainly made some acutely uncomfortable. It was a hard skill to learn. Holding the sheep right, for a start, is an art in itself. Then the strain on my back was agony and driving the blade-shears used many muscles I had never even felt before. After three days I was getting quite a speed up and reached a tally of over ninety a day, which I thought was pretty good for nineteen, but alongside me was a seventy-year-old who was shearing a hundred or more and talking all the time, too.

I kept the skill up until I was thirty, then I found it was too much like hard labour so I retired. By then I could shear about seventy or eighty of my own sheep a day, but one of my sons came back from Australia a really good shearer able to do over 200. Now in middle age, he gets a gang in too.

The technique is to hold the sheep in such a fashion that it does not struggle and yet at the same time the skin remains taut, then run the blade up towards the throat to open the fleece. I learnt with hand-shears which were hard work and made it difficult to take off the last half inch but in those days it was considered that shearing-machines got too close to the skin which made the sheep vulnerable to bad weather. Nowadays all shearing is by machine, a sort of giant hair-clipper is used, but the technique of throwing and holding the sheep is the same. The bent-over position is also the same and the pain which it triggers off in the back muscles hasn't changed either. After half a day's work, the ache was indescribable. It used to take me about a week to work myself into a comfortable action, by which time my flock was finished.

Today, if I wish to give my New Zealand and Australian visitors something to talk about, I show them how I shear at Tangley. In Australia, the sheep are shorn in a wool-shed, specially designed for the purpose with pens in which the sheep can be held overnight in case of rain. The wool is handled by experts and sorted into grades. All imperfections are removed from the fleeces and great pride is taken in the finished product.

I employ a visiting gang of New Zealanders who have to shear in the open, the wool is then rolled up and sent away to be dealt with by the Wool Board, which handles all grading and sales. In Antipodian eyes, our sheep-handling is appalling, yet we get almost the same price for our wool.

The reason for our seeming indifference to wool quality is that it is a minor crop for us. In Australia, the wool would be at least half a sheep's total return, whereas in my case, it accounts for hardly 10 per cent. Today's price for English wool is about fifty pence per lb, while that for lamb-meat is nearly double. My ewes produce about 6 lbs of wool but nearly 60 lbs of lamb-meat on average, so I obviously concentrate on meat production.

A sheep does not produce both high quality wool and milk. Broadly speaking a heavily-woolled sheep with both head and feet covered is a poor milker, does not have many lambs and does not nurture them well. As a result the main lamb-rearing crosses in Britain, which you can see in every lowland field, all have clean heads and legs. Besides, if they have used all their resources producing lambs and milk, they will have little left over for wool.

Shearing is becoming very expensive, costing nearly half the value of the wool; it would be a pleasure to dispense with it altogether and various attempts have been made to reduce the burden. The Australians have devised what they call a shearing table on which sheep could be held while being shorn, in a position which would avoid the shearer having to bend his back. This was invented during a shearers' strike, when the squatters found they were ruining their health doing the shearing themselves, but these tables were soon discarded once the strike was settled. There are also experiments being conducted with a chemical treatment which would cause the wool either to drop off or to pull off easily. I don't know if this would mean having to rake up fleeces in the paddock afterwards and then bale them like hay.

There is a breed of sheep called the Wiltshire Horn which sheds its wool before the normal shearing time and I suppose it might be possible to introduce that quality into our existing breeds. The Wiltshire Horn is used at the moment as a crossing sire for fat-lamb production but it is not very prolific, nor is it a good milker.

In New Zealand they are concentrating on improving shearing techniques, rather than on changing the sheep. Godfrey Bowen, a New Zealander, has set a whole new style of shearing which is being copied now all over the world. His secret is a close study of the sheep's anatomy; he has designed a series of strokes or blows with the shears which follow the animal's conformation and by using this technique he has himself managed to shear well over 400 in an eight-hour day.

But I always remember that in New Zealand we used to separate ewes from lambs before we sheared. By the time the ewes were turned out of the shearing-sheds, many of the lambs had been mis-mothered and never thrived afterwards. My lambs have always been more important. I think I'll stick to my methods.

July

July used to be a quiet month, sandwiched between haymaking and harvesting: a time for a young farmer to marry and for the men to have a holiday, for up to thirty years ago the earliest spring barley would not have been cut until the first week in August. Harvests start earlier nowadays but none have ever been so early as in the year of the great drought, 1976, when I had finished the whole of mine by the end of the month, for the first time in anyone's memory.

That drought hardly bears thinking about. There had been no rain since April, by mid-July I had harvested the winter barley and was starting on the wheat. There was no grass and the sheep were existing on hay and water. As rainless day followed rainless day, the grass became browner and browner and the land cracked further and further, I began to think that this would be how the end of the world would come. Not in a chaos of tempest, flood and earthquake, but in a denial of moisture. There was absolutely nothing to be done except to sell all the sheep I could, and hope that it would rain before the last of the hay ran out.

During the worst of this heat wave I travelled up to the Tweed valley which I found to be an oasis of lush pasture. I stayed with a friend and he told me that he did not know how he could get his grass eaten off. As it happened, I said, I could let him have 500 store lambs off really hard conditions which would be bound to do him well. I did not argue about the price and he certainly saved my bacon. As soon as we had loaded the sheep at Tangley, it began to rain, so my lambs would have been worth five pounds a head more. But a deal is a deal and he had got me out of a nasty spot.

In an ordinary year, my own winter-barley harvest usually starts around the 20th, a good ten days after other farmers', twenty miles south, because at 600 feet, Tangley is always at least a week later getting started than farms around Winchester. I made a great mistake in settling on these mountains years ago but it is too late to argue about that now.

The earlier I can begin to harvest my winter barley the better, for then the work-load is spread more evenly and July is usually warmer, and the days are longer, than in August. Judging when the crop is ripe is always a matter of some dispute. Everyone thinks he knows best. I always spend several days looking at the fields, testing the degree of hardness by biting the grain. Samples can be rubbed out and put through the moisture tester. The trouble with this system is that picking a fair sample by hand is impossible.

I have a very good drier but the secret of good harvesting is to use it as little as possible. Too much heat costs a lot of money and will ruin germination for malting and seed. It is possible to dry any grain however damp by simply putting on more heat, but the art of the job is letting the grain ripen in the field until it is well dried-down before it is cut.

Slightly unripe grain is very hard to dry because it is still full of sap. Once it has ripened in the field a heavy rain will raise the moisture but this is pure water and will dry out very easily. I did not learn drying techniques quickly, and spoilt hundreds of tonnes of grain before I had the tools and the knowledge to do the job.

The determining factor for combining is the degree of moisture in the crop from dew or rain. The machines will thrash out damp grain but if the straw is also damp, they don't make a very good job of it: the crop comes into the combine in great lumps, the machine begins to shudder, there are loud bangs and sometimes it comes to a stop, blocked solid. Freeing it can take an hour or more and lead to a great deal of bad temper.

The first combine-harvesters to be able to cut and thresh out grain from a standing crop were built about sixty years ago in the United States but they are now of world-wide usage and have been adapted to cope with our generally humid harvests. Even the first one I had, which had been designed with no thought for European conditions, coped quite well. But it did break down. I bought it second-hand in 1940 but it had been imported from the States some years before. It was built like a tank and took three men to work it. While the Battle of Britain raged overhead, we battled with the monster on the ground. It made an awful noise but that drowned the sound of gunfire, and gave us an added incentive to get it going again so that we could not hear the strife.

My modern combine costs me about £30,000 and I always have at least two, which means an outlay of £60,000 plus £15,000 for my drier, quite an investment for about four weeks' work a year. But I would never be reliant on just one, even with quite a small acreage, for my nerves could never stand the frustration of not harvesting when the grain was ready and the day fine. Something just has to be moving. Modern combines do break down but not very often, and when they do most agents run a good stock of spares. But I have driven hundreds of miles during a harvest to get the odd part they did not stock and the strain is great.

Combining cannot start till the dew has dried. Once it has begun, however, I hope to run my machines through the dinner- and tea-breaks for these are often the best and driest times of the day. Usually the farmer himself takes over at these moments but I haven't driven a combine for some twenty years, much though I would like to, because of the disasters which befell me last time I did. The crop was grass seed and I had a complicated set of attachments on the combine which made it quite tricky to operate. The early machines had had a driving system like a tractor which I understood well, but this was a new sophisticated type with hydraulic controls. There were two of them on a bar in front of me. One controlled the speed and the other the height of the knife, identical little levers very close together. The field was rather steep and the machine began to gather speed so I pulled what I thought was the speed control but this only raised the knife from the crop, which made it go faster. Then I pulled the other lever and we went faster still because, I was told afterwards, I had over-ridden the stop, whatever that meant. The only way to avoid a very nasty accident was to turn across the crop and run slightly uphill. This worked but what with the speed, and the knife by this time being down again, I brought the whole works to a shuddering, and completely jammed, halt, which took a couple of hours to clear. After listening to my men's sarcastic comments, I told them I would never drive at mealtimes again and I haven't. But I would still like to. After all a combine costs nearly as much as a Rolls Royce and I would certainly drive a Rolls if I had one.

Grain in the British climate is usually thrashed pretty damp at 18 per cent to 22 per cent moisture content. For safe storage it should be below 16 per cent moisture so driers are needed, as are winnowing machines to take the rubbish

105

out of the sample. In this climate there are few days when the grain, once ripe, can be stored straight off the combine, because the relative humidity of the atmosphere is too high. It is little use waiting for that last drop in moisture which may never happen.

I still possess the remains of a cold-air drying system, of which I was one of the pioneers. The principle here was that the grain was spread out straight from the combine on to a floor in which ducts had been laid. Cold air was blown through these ducts for days and days until the grain gradually lost its moisture. This was a most inexact operation because the humidity of the air is infinitely variable and so is that of the grain. Air will blow through dry grain at a much higher velocity than it will through damp, and it was impossible in practice to make sure that all the grain was of uniform humidity. In consequence drying was very uneven indeed. The only sure recommendation for the cold-air system is that grain continually blown does not go mouldy but it seldom produces an easily saleable moisture content, and there are always pockets of damp where the air has been unable to circulate.

My first hot-air drier over forty years ago was a coke-fired Heath Robinson affair and I borrowed a thermometer off a scientist to control the temperature. This used to show an input heat of about 400°F, and some of the grains exposed to the blast used to char. But it dried a great deal of corn and much of it germinated and even malted. Then I bought a thermostatically controlled outfit, and discovered from the instructions that no seed grain should be exposed to more than 120°F.

Over the years combine output has run far ahead of my driers' capacity which has meant either putting up the temperature in order to dry more grain faster or having to run a night shift to clear the decks for the next morning. I was usually the night shift, and used to set the machines to run the grain through automatically while I watched television or went to sleep. I never got this quite right. On one occasion there was a blockage which meant that when I checked up, about ten tonnes of grain, two hours' drying time, were in heaps all over the floor. On a modern plant, howling sirens warn you of any trouble but I bet they would never work whilst I was in charge.

I have now invested in a ten tonne-an-hour drier. My two combines have a joint output of about twelve tonnes an hour, sometimes a bit more. As there is seldom less than three hours before combining starts at about eleven a.m. and an hour or two after they have finished at night, it is no real trouble for the drier to keep up and for me to get my sleep undisturbed.

Combining leaves rows of straw behind on the fields which I like to burn off although I know that many people object to this activity. However I always believe that those who come to live in the country from choice should accept the fact that it is a workshop, where processes which upset them are essential. One of these concerns straw-burning. Modern arable land produces several million tonnes of straw a year for which there is no viable market. Far more is produced than can be used for industrial processes of which the commonest is making paper. Most large arable farms have little stock and as straw is a high-volume, low-density product it does not pay to haul it to the livestock districts for bedding or feed. It does not break down easily in the soil, even when mixed with slurry. Anyway, modern systems of animal husbandry tend to use slats on which to bed the animals and pumps to get rid of the slurry. As straw is not needed for turning into dung, for feeding or for industrial use, the only thing left is to burn it.

In no way do I defend careless straw-burning. But if sufficient attention is given to firebreaks and to burning against the wind, no damage need accrue to trees, hedges or anything else. The problem is compounded by the very success of modern cereal farming: the crops are very thick so there is much more straw and it burns all the more freely.

If I have been lucky enough to get the winter barley harvested quickly and the straw burnt off as the combines leave the field, I start sowing seeds for the next year's pasture. There was a craze for doing this directly on the freshly burnt surface, using a specialised seed-drill but it did not work well at Tangley. There were too many stones which forced the drill-shares out of the ground and a number of weeds grew and competed with the grass. I tried this new method several times and as a result had quite a few failures. I always envy the success others have with techniques I am unable to master. Instead I now follow the combines with the plough and try to get the grass seeds in before the soil moisture can dry out, as it so often does at this time of year. My aim is to plough, harrow, and roll down with each implement chasing the other up the furrow in succession; I then sow grass seeds on the rolled ground. After which I roll again. This constant rolling should ensure a really firm seedbed which is an absolute necessity for success. For grass it should be firmer than for any other crop. The more winter barley I grow, the more work can be done in the longer July days, the less pressure there will be on the next two months.

Once the winter-barley harvest is out of the way, I must turn my attention to the remaining standing crops. Badly infested ones have already been sprayed but in a few fields there will be waving heads of wild oats which have escaped the chemicals and now is the time to pull these out by hand, practically the only manual field-work still done on my farm. It is cheaper to pull these out than to drench the whole field in expensive chemical. The task at first sight is rather like baling out the Atlantic with a teaspoon, it takes a long time to make an impression. The gang is usually made up of teenage school children, girls are very conscientious, under the charge of an experienced adult. They are apt to take a long time gossiping under a hedge, particularly on a hot day, but once they get going they considerably reduce the numbers and are gradually working themselves out of a job. Five years ago they had nearly six weeks' work but now they can make a visible effect in ten days. There will always be a few wild oats, as the birds bring them in from neighbouring fields. You can see them in lines under the electric power-cables where the birds were resting while digesting.

Oats both wild and tame are tolerant of acid soil which is why they grow well at Tangley. In fact if clumps of wild ones appear they usually indicate that the lime status of the soil is falling. Another sign is sheep's sorrel in the stubbles. To assess the degree of weed infestation and to see how well my crops have performed, I ride on the combine in every field. A bare patch with little grain but a great deal of weed is usually the sign of some chemical deficiency in the soil.

My first thought is that the land needs liming again. It was heavily limed in the eighteenth century when they mined the chalk from beneath the topsoil and spread it over the fields. Now I buy lime in from a commercial pit, grind it up and spread it by machine every six or seven years, a vital but expensive job.

It is most important that I know about the quantity and spread of weeds on my farm at this time of year. Theoretically after thirty years of chemical control, there should be few if any weeds, but they do still persist. The other day I noticed quite a reasonable show of poppies in a field where I had not seen them for years. Obviously to kill every single one by successive sprayings with selective chemicals would be impossible and expensive. The art is to balance cost against return and to decide which crops can tolerate a few more weeds, where they have got out of hand, and where they seem to be on the increase. A broad approach is essential. Don't imagine that I am condemning chemicals as aids to farming; they have been a wonderful boon and one of the greatest factors in increasing our yields in the last thirty years, but it is knowing when to use which chemical which is crucial to success.

One of the most persistent weeds I have been plagued with is tall oat-grass, popularly known as onion couch. This can spread either from the seeds which fall just before the crop is ripe, or from the bulbous roots which seem to be able to multiply in a clump, much as do shallots, hence the name onion couch. The seedlings are very easily killed by autumn cultivations but the onions or bulbs are much more of a problem. If they are attacked by conventional means, say cultivators or harrows, the clumps are broken up and each separate bulb is set free to build up another clump. The only time I ever had success with cultivators was in a dry April when the bulbs, once exposed, dried out and died. But this meant that there was little chance of getting a crop that summer. At the start of the war I took over a lot of land infested with this weed and had the greatest difficulty in reducing the population. If this onion couch weed appears in grass sheep will graze the leaves, and if they are grazed hard enough and long enough the bulbs are in the end unable to recover. But it takes a long time, a matter of years. To attempt to kill the bulbs by autumn cultivation is a waste of time as they have been refreshed by a summer's growth and can stand a long period of exposure without harm.

This last year I had an outstanding success spraying them with a new chemical about ten days before harvest, using the tracks through the crop used for previous treatments. The 150 acres I treated are now absolutely clean, I did not find one bulb that survived. The point about spraying just before the harvest is that the plant is caught with the maximum foliage exposed to the chemical and thus at its most vulnerable. If I can get this job done on about July 10th, few seeds will have been dropped and the land will remain clean for years, but not I fear for ever. There are bound to be a few survivors but fortunately onion couch does not spread very rapidly.

It would of course be much simpler to apply the weed-killer from the air. But the chemical used would kill all green things and there is such a thing as wind-drift. I insure against this damage now but a few years ago I was using another spray to kill a common weed. A retired gentleman whose garden bordered the field said that the spray had damaged his currants and rasp-berries. They certainly looked a bit sick, although I could not be sure that the cause was not blight or aphids. So we arrived at a compromise and he seemed mollified. Some months later I met his wife and asked her how her husband was. 'Very well,' she said. 'Picking the fruit used to wear him out and he had to hire labour as well. Thanks to you, we were able to pick enough for our own use, there was no need for hiring and hard work. For the first time in ten years the garden made a profit.'

Another July task is to harvest any oilseed rape I may have grown. It's that vivid yellow plant over six foot tall which can be seen flowering at the end of April into May. Farmers mainly grow it because of the heavy subsidy it attracts from the Common Agricultural Policy. The EEC hope that by growing rape, the Community will become more self-sufficient in vegetable oils, that it will cut out competition from imported oilseed and that it will provide a useful alternative to cereals which are already in surplus. A common rotation on the Continent is oilseed rape, wheat, winter barley, and then oilseed rape again. There are problems though. It is a brassica, and the pigeons are excessively fond of the leaves, particularly in cold weather; unless checked they can eat the heart of a crop. Being tall it is vulnerable to late snow which will flatten it out, which happened in April 1981. The seed-pods are very brittle, and a strong wind will make them shatter, so wasting a lot of the crop and infesting the soil with the seeds for years to come. Some appeared in one of my fields twenty-five years after rape was last harvested there. The growing crop needs considerable attention with chemicals, and is usually cut and laid on the ground before combining so as to make sure all the seeds are ripening evenly. There is evidence that the rape plant is subject to soil-borne diseases which will last over the two-year break when the field is in cereals. In Schleswig Holstein where much of the cultivation of the crop has been developed, there are reports of very serious failures due to disease.

My own reluctance to grow the crop on any scale is more to do with the fact that the subsidy for growing it is about 60 per cent of the final price received than with the hazards of harvest; a very dangerous situation in which to be placed with any sizeable acreage. The politics of oilseeds also affect me materially, affecting my pigs and their soya-bean meal. Soya beans are used in margarine, in cooking-oils and for making pig and cattle feeds. Every tonne of my pig ration contains between 10 and 15 per cent of soya-bean meal. The beans are imported whole and then crushed in this country and also elsewhere in Europe. The meal is high in protein and is a good safe feed. At the moment soya-bean meal enters the EEC duty free which suits me but infuriates other vested interests. The dairy lobby claims that soya oil, from which margarine is made, competes with butter. Olive oil and other oilseed interests want protection against cheap imports of soya beans and, to cap it all, some Community interests complain that the soya meal is the basis of dairy-cow feeds which encourages yet more surplus milk, which has to be exported at ever-greater cost.

So far soya beans have not yet been clobbered for duty, but pressure is building up from the vested interests. If they are successful, then it will inevitably mean dearer pig and cattle feed (and it is used in some hen feeds too). The obvious answer would be to grow more soya in Europe but although it will ripen in parts of France it is not so profitable a crop as cereals. Yields are not high and it would probably need a subsidy at least as large as that for oilseed rape to encourage people to grow it, which would be about £120 an acre.

The question of soya imports is an urgent one at present in EEC politics. If the vested interests forced a duty to be levied on it, or if it were raised in price because of a subsidy, or if it were no longer available, it would greatly upset the economics of many branches of livestock farming, including that of my pigs. The subtle interplay of duty, subsidy, price and levy has to be considered in its widest ramifications in every country in the EEC if all the repercussions are to be taken into account.

In a normal July there are three main harvests to be gathered in: winter barley, oilseed rape and grass seed. I have been growing grass seeds for many years but in a spasmodic way, as they are a gambler's crop with considerable competition from New Zealand and Europe. For about half the time the market is oversupplied, and it is not worth harvesting, but on occasions I have hit the jackpot, although it has been made harder now by Common Market regulations which control the certification of all seed crops. It used to be possible to have a pasture sown with a particular variety and leave it down for several years before taking a seed crop. Then the seed, once harvested, could be offered on the free market to the highest bidder. Nowadays the rules are that the crop has to be registered on sowing down, and contracted to a specific merchant. The prices are not fixed on a man-to-man basis but by agreement between the NFU seeds committee and the merchants. It is right out of my control, and I don't like it.

Harvesting grass seed is also an uncontrollable operation as often as not. The crop is heavily fertilised with nitrogen so that it falls completely flat, as though a roller had passed over it. It is then cut with a combine while it is still green. The harvested seed looks pretty mucky as it is still full of moisture, but it can now be dried. However if the weather breaks before I have managed to cut and combine the grass, the seed will drop out and sprout and then the whole enterprise is doomed to failure. Thirty or forty acres of seed harvest is enough for anyone.

Despite being an extremely busy month for all farmers, who are frantically combining their winter wheat, oilseed rape and grass seeds, spraying with weed-killers, overseeing their livestock and getting their harvested land ready for next year's crops, it has been chosen as the month for the Royal Show, a major event in the farming calendar. I say this with some qualification for it is perfectly possible to farm successfully all one's life and never visit the Royal, or any other of the lesser shows around the country. This is a matter of some concern to those who run the Royal Agricultural Society which was founded about 150 years ago with the motto 'Practice with Science'. In their early days the Royal and the other show societies, were the instigators of much farming improvement. They demonstrated excellence in livestock and various methods of husbandry. But then their functions were usurped by the State, which provided advisory services and also by the various supply industries which began to initiate their own research. The Royal never had the funds to develop these activities and even its relations with governments were taken over by the National Farmers' Union. So the Royal became a rather snobbish enclave of the farming Establishment; a governor was senior to a member because he paid a higher subscription, the peerage and landed gentry dominated the council. The standards for the competitions between the livestock were decided by the respective breed societies, whose assessments were based on visual judgment. As indeed they still are today.

But in the real world the development of livestock has, over the last forty years, been directed towards increased production of meat and milk with breed societies' standards of purity, elegance and conformation very much in second place. Such criteria as feed-conversion ratios and weight-for-age are the result of years of trials under controlled conditions. They are also the result of some fairly indiscriminate cross-breeding. They have little to do with show-ring standards.

It is possible to improve yields and performance by selection within a breed, but it is a long slow job. A cross between two separate breeds endows the progeny with hybrid vigour and significantly increases its production. This hybrid vigour or heterosis has been well known for years and the ewes I farm benefit from it. The difficulty is to fix this increased productivity in subsequent generations.

Barring the mountain breeds of sheep there are very few pure-bred truly commercial livestock populations now. Poultry and pigs are almost entirely the result of cross-breeding. The dairy herd, although predominantly Black and White Friesian, is being infiltrated with Holstein blood from North America. There are still breed societies which will produce pure-bred sires for crossing. But an increasing number of farmers are producing cross-bred bulls particularly for beef-cattle. This is a very recent development. Until a few years ago bulls were only allowed to be used if they were pure-bred and had been licensed by

111

the Ministry of Agriculture. The standards then were all of the prize ring. Then a Minister suddenly took the view that farmers were adult enough to know what they were doing with their own stock. Who could quarrel with that?

There are still pedigree livestock at the Show and I like to look at them, but I guess fewer than 10 per cent of those attending bother. So why do they go? It is a social occasion. There is some good horse-jumping. Parachutes fall out of the sky and foxhounds gallop around the ring. There are also demonstration plots and livestock units such as can be seen in many other places where conditions are often very different from those at Kenilworth.

The bill for most of this is picked up by the trade stands, which really means by us, their farmer customers. There are some 600 of them selling everything from combine-harvesters to double glazing. They provide tea and harder refreshment for the footsore crowds. At some of the stands there is a strict culling process: the common-or-garden types get tea and cakes on the ground floor, the upper storeys are reserved for the Establishment with a proper catering service.

The most striking innovation has been Bankers' Row, where the banks and the Stock Exchange have spread themselves in a series of pavilions where customers are lavishly entertained. For the banks to give anything away must be a sign that they are doing too well out of us. For myself I expect nothing but austerity from a bank. But then times have changed, banks are selling money to farmers like washing-powder.

Does all this expensive flummery mean anything to farming? Not much I fear. In fact it could do harm by demonstrating that farmers' life styles, as shown by their expenditure and their cars, at least half of which are of foreign make, underline that they are not nearly so badly off as the NFU tries to pretend.

August

I don't enjoy August. The days are getting measurably shorter, there is a smell of autumn in the air, and it is often a very wet month which does not make harvesting any easier. I can usually start on some early spring barley during the first week and then follow with wheat which is generally ready to combine around the 18th. These dates are very dependable and hardly seem to alter, whatever the time of sowing or weather during the preceding months. Only the exceptional drought in 1976 brought harvest weeks further forward.

Of August's thirty-one days, there are seldom more than twelve when combining is possible, and so I need two combines each capable of about twenty acres a day, including time allowed for breakdowns, to make sure that I finish in time. Harvesting wheat and barley is like picking pears: there are seldom more than two or three days between the crop being ripe and its starting to deteriorate.

Wheat is particularly at risk. The ear is vertical and each grain is enclosed in a soft chaff with the open end facing the sky. Once the grain is ripe it is looking for a chance to germinate and if the chaff becomes really damp it will do just this. Once germinated, wheat is no good for milling, although it will do for biscuits or animal feed, moreover it becomes difficult to dry and yield falls quite significantly.

Some wheats are particularly vulnerable to sprouting. I grew a new variety once, Holdfast was its name, and during a wet period the grain sprouted so badly that the ears turned green with the shoots pushing out to the light. I harvested and dried it. The result was an excellent animal feed, almost pure wheat malt. The malting process is to soak grain, germinate it, and then dry it when it becomes very sweet and sugary.

Some wheats don't wait until they are ripe before they sprout. One, Huntsman, will do so while still green, but as it is a very heavy yielder and a good feed-grain there is some sense in growing a few fields and taking a chance on the sprouting. Farmers are always foolish optimists.

Sprouting is nothing new. Before I started using a combine all wheat was cut with a binder well before the grain was ripe. The sheaves were stooked, or aisled as the locals term it, in eights and tens and left for ten days to a fortnight to dry off before being carted to a stack. The stooks would sprout in a wet time because the rain lodged in the upright ears. But there was little that could be done about it. The wheat had to be cut before it was really ripe. Had it been ripe much of it would have been shaken out while being cut and carried. If it had been stacked while still unripe it would heat and the grain be spoilt.

I used to enjoy driving a binder. First with horses when working for others, and then sitting on my own binder while my tractor towed it. There was a great satisfaction seeing each nicely-tied sheaf being thrown out of the works. I weighed one or two and worked out the quantity of grain which each contained and then counted the sheaves to estimate just how good harvest would be. I generally made the forecast too optimistic.

Binders are seldom seen today except in the far west of Scotland where oats are still cut and stooked, unless a farmer wishes to produce straw for thatching. For this the farmer can expect to receive between eighty and a hundred pounds a tonne so it is a worthwhile by-product. I have toyed with the notion of buying an old binder and making some thatching straw myself. My men don't like the idea. They would have to learn how to stook the sheaves and pitch them on to trailers and build the stacks. This is quite an art. The whole point of the exercise is to keep the sheaves pointing upwards as they are being laid so that if any

114

water gets in it will run out again. A well-built stack should stay dry for several weeks without being thatched.

One of my neighbours saved some thatching straw last year, and told me that he lost at least a quarter of the wheat he should have harvested. The grain was not quite mature enough when he cut it, and then there were losses from the weather and from vermin: rooks, rats and mice. Rooks in particular will attack a stack, pulling the sheaves to pieces. After they have given up, mice and rats take over. Rook attacks are much worse these days because the number of stacks is tiny compared with what it used to be. The birds can concentrate their forces and once they have tasted freshly-cut wheat they will not leave the sheaves or stacks alone. They don't find the standing crop quite so easy but here they are helped by pigeons. These have a technique of flopping into the crop and knocking a few ears to the ground. It does not take them long to push down a wide area once they have started, and then the rooks join in. Sometimes they will start at the edge of a field and work inwards. Birds are assisted in their attacks by a disease called eyespot which weakens wheat straw so that it collapses and the crop looks as flat as if a roller had passed over it. Eyespot collapse is distinguishable from storm damage or an excess of nitrogen for these latter create a distinct tangling effect. It is very distressing to find a wheat crop on which you have lavished care and any amount of money for many months and which looked marvellous in late July, suddenly collapse in an untidy heap at the beginning of August with the grain still green. Worse is to follow. If the crop has gone down early there is a danger that the plants will shoot again from the roots, and by the time the main crop is ready for harvest the new shoots have green corn on them which quite spoils the sample. This is a particular danger with barley but can now be coped with to some extent at harvest-time by spraying with a dessicant which will dry up the green stuff.

Where the crops have managed to stand up straight right to the end of the season, they will be much thicker than they used to be. A traditional harvest sport was to shoot rabbits running from the declining square of standing crop as the field was being finished. There are however many fewer rabbits now for myxomatosis has kept the numbers down and the crops are also much denser. I still find rabbits in a thin crop where they have room to move but very seldom in a thick one. Most fields though will produce a roe or fallow deer. These like living in the standing corn and feeding off the ears. They lie very close while the field is being cut and only jump at the last minute. I won't allow them to be shot. The pellets of a shotgun will usually only wound and not kill outright unless the animals are very close. A rifle carries too far to be safe to use in Hampshire. However the deer are beginning to make quite an impression in some parts of the farm, and something will have to be done before too long.

Barley and oats, while not so stiff in the straw as wheat, will not sprout so easily. Their ears hang downwards when ripe and the oat has its seed protected by moisture-shedding chaff, hence its popularity in western Scotland and Wales where it is the only grain crop which can stand the climate. At one time it was considered sound practice to undersow both barley and oats with grass seeds. The grass would grow in the shelter of the cereal and after harvest would soon come away in the stubbles. This has gone by the board now. The weed-killing sprays massacre clovers and the density of modern crops is such that the grass would be smothered. This wasn't always the case. For many years I grew barley continuously and part of the process was to undersow it with rye-grass and trefoil. The theory was that the grass mixture supplied humus to the stubbles and so kept the land in better heart for the next crop. Nothing however performed as the book said it should. Sometimes the barley smothered the grass and there was none to be seen after harvest. At others the reverse happened. Once or twice I had fields which at harvest looked just like a hay field. On a hot dry day the combines would go through them quite well, but if they were damp it was a miserable job. After a few years I gave up undersowing and never had any reduction in yield. I can only conclude that this particular technique was a waste of time. It had been originated by a very well-known farmer at whose feet we used to sit. He had got through the depression by growing continuous barley undersown every year. He believed in it most firmly, and as in most human activity faith is the surest way to success.

The point about continuous barley-growing was that, in the circumstances of those days, it provided a regular, if small annual income off every acre of the farm. Wheat, although yielding much better than barley, could only be grown in rotation and so the overall cereal income was higher. I never knew why it was possible to grow barley continuously and not wheat. Probably the barley plant was tolerant of disease to a greater extent than that of wheat, also we were using spring-sown barley which gave the land time for the pests to die out before resowing took place. Continuous wheat-growing has been tried in the past many times but has always failed through disease. One of the most common is called Take All. The crop appears to develop well but a month before harvest the plants turn white and the grain never forms in the ear. Since the advent of chemicals some farmers have been growing continuous wheat for three to five years, with what they claim to be a fair degree of success, but at considerable expense. I seldom grow wheat more than two years running. In France, even with the most modern aids to plant protection, wheat is hardly ever grown more than once in a rotation. I think French arable farming is by far the best in Europe and probably in the world.

The farmer I have mentioned above, the undersowing barley guru, was, as are most pioneers, an original thinker. He grew malting barley, and for his first seeding went to the local maltings and bought a selection of best barleys. These he mixed together and planted, saving his seed every year. No nonsense of chasing after new varieties. If it worked in 1922 it would work in 1942 he told me, and I am sure if one stuck to the same principles today one could be equally successful.

I had one block of land from 1940 to 1968 on which I had to grow barley as there were no break-crops available. The yields varied according to the season and I always made a profit. I sometimes wish I had kept it up, indeed I would have done, had it not been for the competitive spirit of farming. This has always been a very powerful force and is most apparent in August when the harvest is on. It may no longer be a time of rollicking dances and merry village festivities but farmers still rejoice in the quality and quantity of their yields and take enormous pride in their successes. Every farmer wants to grow more crops per acre, more milk per cow, more pigs per sow and more lambs per ewe, than any of his neighbours. They boast about their achievements at meetings and among other farmers. But they very seldom produce any evidence, hard evidence that is, of their results. There are some tall tales going in this neighbourhood of fantastic results, but I don't see my neighbours adding significantly to their silos.

There is a sense of shame if I cannot say, even untruthfully, that all my grain averages three tonnes an acre. This is not enough for some. They claim four tonnes and some are even going higher. No one comes and measures their acreages and their crops. Field acreages are those of the ordnance survey, which includes the hedges and headlands. Farmers deduct these from the total when calculating very generously so that the crop is grown off a smaller acreage than is really the case.

Then again few measure accurately the grain coming into their stores. In any case this is difficult as the equipment for doing this is far from accurate. The best way is to measure the silo and then the bushel weight or specific gravity of the grain, but bushel weight can vary enormously. It is a loose term referring to the density of the grain. The standard for wheat for instance is that a bushel-measure of a standard capacity of 1.28 cubic feet should contain 63 lbs. Should a bushel of wheat weigh only 56 lbs, it would be called a low bushel-weight; if it weighed say 66 lbs, it would be a very high bushel-weight. Just to complicate things a standard bushel of barley weighs 56 lbs and one of oats 40. Officially now the density of grain is measured in kilograms per hectolitre but farmers and merchants still insist on talking in bushels. When I started farming, grain was sold in quarters each of eight bushels. A standard quarter of wheat weighed 8 × 63 lbs = 504 lbs. This could be confusing for newcomers to farming. A naval officer invalided from the service took a neighbouring farm and when working out his first year's profits thought that he was going to be overpaid. He had grown about a ton to the acre and seeing in the press that wheat was worth at that time about five pounds a quarter he worked out that he would have eighty times five pounds as there were eighty quarters of 28 lbs in every ton and not four and a half. Nor did he keep quiet about it. He publicised this overpayment to farmers at a time of national emergency in the press and at meetings; it was some time before the penny dropped. To make it easier for the simple minds outside farming, we are now paid in metric tonnes, but I still think in bushels and quarters. To say nothing of hundredweights. But I do approve of the metric tonne. It weighs 40 lbs less than an imperial one, so naturally I sell everything by it.

In 1981 my barley weight per bushel varied by 20 per cent as between fields. So a fifty-tonne-sized silo could weigh out anything from forty to fifty tonnes of barley. Last year wheat was of very good bushel-weight and the standard silo weighed 10 per cent more. The determining factor in bushel-weight is not really known, but I believe it to be a crop which has been allowed to mature on the straw until it is absolutely ripe. Disease of course can affect it, so can early cutting and so of course can sprouting. Do you now wonder that I do not always believe all those tales I hear when I meet fellow-farmers at shows and markets? How have they worked out their bushels? Their tonnes to the acre?

One way of course of increasing production is to enlarge the size of fields by uprooting hedges and fences. On 500 acres of this farm I have reduced the number of separate fields from twenty-five to eight. Even so the whole area is well wooded. I have left the hedges and the hedgerow trees where the fields are divided by lanes and rights of way. At eye-level the view is much the same as it always was, only the disappearance of the elms has made a significant difference. The removal of the hedges has improved yields and made working the fields more efficient and the hedges themselves have not had to be maintained. This is a costly job and an unnecessary one as on this land the growth in the live hedge is insufficient to provide stock-proof fencing as it does in the Midlands for instance. The hedges used to contain rabbits and still do harbour a variety of other birds and mammals which take a toll of the growing crops.

Hedges, particularly hedgerow trees, will suck sustenance from the soil far beyond the area they cover above ground. The first cut of a combine going round will yield half or less of the crop further into the field. These are the considerations which the conservationist lobby forgets. Why should a farmer maintain an obsolete countryside for the aesthetic pleasure of people who seldom live there?

Once I was plagued by poachers who were able to get into my woods by slinking up a narrow belt of trees. I solved that one by grubbing up the trees, and the outcry reverberated for weeks. Not because I was spoiling the countryside but because I had removed the poachers' line of advance or retreat. I wasn't too worried about the game, but suspected that we were losing the odd lamb.

Hedges were planted originally, for the most part, as field boundaries at the time of the Enclosure Acts about 200 years ago. They were seldom used for controlling livestock in this part of the country because they do not grow thick enough. Nor do we have ditches around here for carrying away water for on chalkland surface water is absorbed into the permeable soil. Nobody hedges and ditches these days; hedging is a lost art in the south of England, all most farmers do to keep their few boundary-fence hedges in order, is to trim them mechanically.

What however we do have are hazel coppices. Thousands of acres of these were once planted to make sheep-hurdles and thatching-spars – the split stems for fastening down thatch. Hazel coppices were interplanted with oak or beech which did not make very good growth, so like a number of other farmers, I have cleared a fair acreage. Once cleared you can find the old furrows.

What the conservationists do not realise is that the countryside has been continually changing to fit the farming needs of the time. For instance, there have never been hedgerows on Salisbury Plain, where arable farming started in these islands in prehistoric times, for by the time enclosures were all the rage, the land was exhausted and only suitable for grazing. I believe that there is no finer view than a well-farmed countryside but this can only be achieved if farming is profitable; it must also be understood that farming is a live and developing industry and cannot be limited in its adaptation to the times.

Nowhere is this more evident than in the labour force. August was once the highlight of the farming year, a time of immense excitement and activity throughout the neighbourhood when most were roped in to help with the harvest. Even in my time, just before the war, it took nine men to harvest fifteen acres a day on this farm: three on the tractors, two pitchers in the field to throw the sheaves up into the trailers, one on the trailer to load it so that the sheaves did not fall off and three men on the stack-building. Even then the job would only be half done: the stack would eventually have to be thatched and it would take six men at least all day to thrash. In all I used to employ twenty-two men on my present acreage.

By contrast, one of my combines with one trailer-driver and one man on the drier can harvest fifteen acres in about half a day and be ready to tackle an equal amount in the afternoon. I now employ six men and my output of grain is about three times what it was. If I were not so old and idle I could manage with four plus a couple of students at harvest time.

119

Much nonsense is talked about the skills of the old-time farm-worker. There were a few naturally skilled men, particularly amongst those working with livestock, but for the most part, the great majority were very unskilled indeed. Education in the rural areas up to the outbreak of the Great War in 1914 was appalling: all the best village brains fled to the towns, those who remained were often uncomplaining plodders, happy to continue in the old ways.

Mind you, some of the old farm-hands were splendidly crusty characters who quite dominated their bosses. A friend of mine once took me to see a new combine-harvester which he'd just bought and which was working on a remote farm of his run by a very good foreman. When we arrived the foreman was nowhere to be seen. My friend then ordered the driver off the machine so that he could drive it himself, with me up beside him. As luck would have it, my friend managed to lurch into a pit, where the combine stuck. 'Quick John,' he said, 'Mitchell mustn't see us.' We were out of the field as if the devil was after us, so I never heard what Mitchell had to say.

Some of the real tyrants used to be the shepherds particularly on the arable farms of Hampshire and Wiltshire where the sheep were the most important component on the farm. They produced the dung which grew the crops. In one case the farmer had found himself with a rick of hay surplus to the flock's requirements for that winter, so he sold it to a racehorse trainer. A few days later he was talking to the shepherd who mentioned the sale of the hay, which he had heard about through the farm grapevine. 'Was it true Governor?' he asked. 'Yes,' said the farmer. 'I sold it because we had a lot more than you'd need for the winter.' 'True,' said the shepherd, 'but I must give in my notice.' 'Why?' said the boss. 'I reckons to be consulted on matters of that sort.' He was a good shepherd so the farmer gave the racehorse man a profit to cancel the deal.

I had Scottish shepherds for a while but I found them almost as difficult as the old Wiltshire ones. One man ordered me out of the lambing-field when I was checking on his work, and I found another was grazing my ewes on a neighbour's farm during the hours of darkness. This latter was certainly looking after my interests. But it took some explaining away when it was discovered. This same man used to have a very forceful dog to which the sheep were accustomed. It was not one of the strong-eyed dogs that you see on television sheep-dog trials, slinking close to the ground and dominating the ewes with a power of the canine eye. If the sheep did not move quickly enough this dog used to give a bark or even a bite.

I lent some of my sheep for the local fête where they had a real expert demonstrating how to work four dogs. They could do nothing with my sheep, which just stamped their feet or even charged the dogs if they got too close. After a while the dog expert gave up and I told the shepherd to take the sheep home in the lorry. All he said to the dog which was at his side was, 'Put the buggers in the box Bob.' Bob dashed away barking and chased the sheep up into the lorry and that was that.

Some of those old hands were wayward, independent men of great character whose methods were often idiosyncratic to say the least whereas the present-day farm-worker is a technician of a very high order indeed, who carries considerable responsibility, for which I think he is ill rewarded even now. A cowman may have sole charge of a dairy representing an investment of £100,000 at least. Each of my tractor-drivers is looking after a similar investment in plant and production. Shepherds and stockmen have to be able to use the latest antibiotics and chemicals. None of my men has special training. I reckon either I, or my foreman who looks after the arable work and the machinery, know how to tell them what to do, but we expect them to get on with the job without supervision, to act on their own initiative. There are training-courses but I have seldom made use of them. A dealer will send an instructor out to explain a new machine; the veterinary surgeon, with whom I co-operate closely, will see the men know how to use the new drugs. I think I am lucky to have such a loyal and interested labour force. I say interested advisedly. Unless you can make a man take an interest in his work he will not be any good. The easiest way of doing this is to make him solely responsible for his particular job. This sense of responsibility is more potent an incentive than extra money, of which at least a third is taken in tax.

My foreman is equivalent to the managing director of a factory, my men are running specialist units. Many people forget farming is an industry, not an idyllic pastime. But harvesting underlines the subtle difference between farming and a manufacturing industry. My investment in two combines is only put to work for the two harvest months and even then they are not always fully employed. My staff is very busy harvesting and drilling from July to October, after which there is only routine maintenance, the application of chemicals plus a little spring sowing to be done. If I had no sheep or pigs, with which the tractor-drivers lend a hand, there would be little regular winter work which I could give them to do.

Many have looked into the possibility of employing contractors for the busy periods. But the difficulty is that the harvest and sowing season is so short that everyone wants the contractor at the same time, and he has the same difficulty in justifying his investment as does the farmer. It is very different in the US, where, because of the spread in climates, contractors can start combining in Texas in May and finish up across the Canadian border in September.

For some years I had a farm in south Devon which was very early ripening. I sent my combines down there first and they'd finish the harvest, and be back in plenty of time to start at Tangley. But after a year or two the Devon harvest began to match that in Hampshire. I had stepped up yields there in the south by using more fertilisers, and this delayed ripening. So co-ordination ceased to work. A combine is about the biggest single investment any farmer is likely to make, and I have always tried to reduce its cost. The most obvious way to do this is to make it last longer. But it is easier said than done.

When I first became involved in farm machinery it was based on steam-engines and thrashing-machines which were expected to last at least two if not three generations. The earlier combines were the same, mainly built in the US and Canada. There I have seen machines still working which are up to forty years old. Here we seem to have become the slaves of fashion, assisted by some good tax write-offs. After about three years the combine is losing some of its gloss. There are annoying little breakages, the dealer has the parts of course but replacing them in the middle of harvest when the weather is threatening can lead to very high blood-pressure. Then, after a year or two, breakdowns become more serious and the spares are not so readily available.

You might well ask why we do not go in for what the aero-engineers call preventive maintenance. As one who was giving me a hand said to me, 'If they sent planes into the sky without it, there would be a lot of crashes.' There is a good deal in what he said, and I have tried to follow his advice. But the economics of farming do not allow for the complete rebuilding of machines on a fixed time-basis. We always think the bearing will go for another season, and maintain on a hand-to-mouth basis.

Then I find that a new model has come along, the spares situation begins to deteriorate further and the salesman hints that it is time I bought a new machine. He points out that most of my neighbours are re-equipping themselves. He infers that not to keep up with the Jones's, machinery-wise, is a sign of inefficiency. I can resist this as well as most, but then I have a big livestock enterprise which gives me great pleasure and which I can walk my friends around. If I did not have these, I would have nothing to look at on the farm, apart from the growing crops in the summer. The desire to have something to look at which is gleaming and new is the motivation behind many farmers' purchases.

There is an increasing number of farms without any livestock at all. Farmers have been told by various consultants that in a predominantly arable area, such as Hampshire, livestock is not so profitable as cropping. They can show you unarguable figures to prove their point. Then livestock is complicated. The most profitable, cows and pigs, are the most difficult to run successfully. Sheep and beef-cattle hardly pay at all by any standards. Even the dung which was the main reason for which beef-cattle were kept can be replaced by fertilisers and crop residues. If anything goes wrong with a livestock unit it will be at a weekend or a holiday. Several times at Christmas power-cuts or animal accidents have disrupted lunch. While the arable farmer and his men can retire from the scene until the weather improves, the stock-farmer has to be out in it, if only to encourage his staff, a most important point this.

I have suffered as much as anyone from these annoyances and from the occasional labour hiccup. I was going out to dinner one Saturday evening, in the days when I had a dairy herd, when two policemen turned up and said they wanted to lock up my cowman for not paying maintenance to his deserted wife. I paid the bill and deducted it from the man's wages. I didn't fancy milking a hundred cows myself for the rest of the weekend.

In spite of all these arguments I obstinately maintain my livestock. They provide the classic safeguard of not having all my eggs in one basket, although the cereal basket is a very good one at the moment. Farming history shows that the prosperity of grain farmers has fluctuated enormously over the centuries, and that the forty years of good cereal farming we have enjoyed latterly have been an exception. I just don't believe the good life of the grain farmer can last much longer. I have been thinking this for the last thirty years, but every year things have got a little better and, since joining the EEC, very much better. I still have my doubts though, and will be deeply disappointed if I should leave the scene without the disaster having happened. In case it does I am keeping my tackle up to date. If the worst comes to the worst, I should not have to buy a machine for the next twenty years at least. Meanwhile I should be able to keep going with sheep and pigs, fed in part on the cheap grain grown by my bankrupt neighbours.

Sheep dipping is compulsory between June 14th and September 5th to try to stamp out sheep-scab, a disease that has symptoms rather like eczema, bad attacks cause the wool to drop out and sheep to lose condition very badly. It is caused by a mite which is susceptible to modern dips using organo-phosphate and to chemicals like dieldrin and aldrin. Unfortunately however it was found that these powerful chemicals were being transmitted to other forms of life through the food-chain with adverse effect, so they were banned. In America they found that poultry was being given a feed which included mutton fat which was passing on the dieldrin to the chickens and there were well-publicised scares that some predatory birds in England had also suffered poisoning through eating sheep which had been dipped in dieldrin.

Before the ban occurred Scotland, England and Wales had been declared clear of sheep-scab. They might have remained free had it not been for the importation of sheep from Ireland where the scab still existed. Now sheep-scab is back again in mainland Britain and is particularly bad in the South and on moors where supervision is difficult.

Dipping means total immersion for about a minute of every sheep in a flock under the supervision of an inspector of the Ministry of Agriculture. I have my own swim-bath which is about thirty-foot long. After the first year, the sheep get to know the procedure and resist immersion so each one has to be man-handled in.

I have never had scab on my farm, but when I worked in the Argentine I spent much of my time trying to cure scab on both sheep and cattle with some of the very ineffective materials that were available in those days. In one place I was responsible for seeing that 20,000 sheep were dipped once a week for three weeks and every one had to be man-handled into the dip.

When it was thought that the mainland of Britain was free of sheep-scab a few years ago, compulsory dipping was relaxed. However, we still had to rid our sheep of parasites and blow-flies. These lay their eggs on the fleeces, particularly where they are stained by dung, maggots then hatch out which later attack the skin and the flesh beneath, particularly in July and in thundery weather.

Many of us devised spray-races for sheep so they could be showered with a chemical instead of our having to man-handle them into a bath. The spray system was much kinder to the sheep and to the men handling them but it is not acceptable to the Ministry advisers who insist on total immersion now that sheep-scab is back again.

Another common disease in sheep and lambs is foot-rot. The animal goes lame and on examination the feet will be found to be quite literally rotting. It is usually caused by some sort of damage to the foot, a cut or a scald between the two claws of the hoof caused by the friction of long grass on the pastures. It can best be cured by strong disinfectants such as formalin; if it is very bad antibiotic treatment may be necessary. I have always thought that this was a matter for the shepherd. Some appear to have little trouble because they catch the disease in its early stages, but others always seem to be in difficulty. If, for instance, there is a long period of wet weather and the ground is soft, then the feet tend to grow long and this predisposes them to rot. However stony ground like mine keeps the hooves short and healthy.

I don't know what I would do without my pigs and sheep for August can be an aggravating month, alternating between hectic bursts of harvesting activity and restless waiting for the rain to cease. When it is wet, I assuage my frustration by contemplating my livestock. By the middle of August, I should have sold the last of my fat lambs, leaving me with about 20 per cent to be weaned and then sold afterwards for other farmers to fatten. I never think it is worth while to fatten any lambs once they have been weaned. If I have any good feed I like it to be saved back for the ewes. This enables me overall to keep more ewes on the farm, and this is the time of year when they should begin to improve in condition for mating once again.

Lambs do not fatten very well once they have been weaned. They generally start to grow, to put on bone and lose that baby fat which they had earlier. They will get much heavier in time but they really need better feed than grass, particularly August grass which is pretty tired and worn out, unless there has been plenty of rain, which of course I don't want. Ewes though will thrive quite well on shortish commons as long as it is dry. The worst thing for sheep is a wet period when their coats are soaked. For fattening lambs once they are weaned it is really essential to plant a special crop, say, rape or kale, and it is difficult to get a really good result from this unless it is sown before the end of June. As I don't start harvest until mid-July this would mean reserving a field for sheep-feed early in the year, something which is quite out of the question at the present level of land-costs. Every acre must show a return these days.

September

I was about to apply to rent an arable farm in central Hampshire some years ago when the landlord's agent told me that it would be mandatory for me to leave the stubble unploughed for most of the autumn so that partridges could hide and feed in it. But today the whole aim of arable farming is to get rid of the stubble, or crop residue as it is now called, as soon as the grain is harvested. As a result partridges are scarce when shooting begins on September 1st and landowners are spending vast sums of money trying to breed them to restock their shoots.

Popular opinion had it that partridges declined initially because of pesticide poisoning but it is modern farming methods which have diminished their numbers. The weed-seeds on which they used to feed have been largely suppressed and many nesting-sites have been wiped out by the removal of hedges. Early cutting of grass for silage and hay destroys the nests of those birds sitting out in the open fields.

Partridges have also suffered competition from the popularity of the pheasant. The latter is easier to rear, is much bigger and a slower target. Pheasants compete for food with partridges and are even said to drive the latter off their nests. But even if landowners do succeed in breeding more partridges, these birds are hard put to find enough stubble around in September in which to live.

I normally fit spreaders on my combine so that the straw is strewn evenly over the field and will dry out quickly after rain. Barley straw burns very easily but wheat straw is a very different matter. It is tougher and retains sap after the seed has been harvested; it will never burn if it is left in thick unspread rows.

Within a week of harvest my stubble fields ideally should be a black desert and within another week this should have given way to brown earth as the cultivators pass over the land. This cultivation should bury the weed-seeds and the small amount of waste grain which always falls out of the back of the combines. Farmers work themselves into a state about this waste, complain to the manufacturers and blackguard the drivers. But it is more apparent than real for it mostly consists of light grains. These show up in the stubble as lines of green shoots. As all are viable they germinate, but with luck we can plough them in out of harm's way. This waste can be stopped by combining more slowly but, if I did that, I might lose a good deal of fine harvest weather. It is also possible to set the combine so that it takes more of the light grains into the tank, but then these have to be cleaned out afterwards and this slows down the drying process. It is best not to worry about waste but to think about the grain saved.

Stubbles can cause problems. A friend's daughter was being married and he asked me if my nearest field could be left unburnt so that it could be used as a car park. I obliged, only to find that the ladies all complained that the stubble laddered their stockings. Then in the middle of the festivities, which we were enjoying in the garden, someone lit his stubble some distance away and we were all driven indoors by the smuts. The moral of this is that if you live in the country, don't give a wedding in September unless you ask all the farmers for miles around.

At one time every town and village had its fair. There is even a fair ground at Tangley but fifty years ago no one living had seen it, and there were some pretty old inhabitants around. The fairs were based on the farming seasons and the September fairs were a time for changing jobs and trading in sheep and cattle. There used to be a famous fair at Weyhill just down the road until after the end of the last war but even then it was a shadow of its former self. A hundred years ago, tens of thousands of sheep were sold there and it was the selling point for the hops grown in East Hampshire for which brewers used to travel up from the West Country. The stalls where the hops were sold are still there but the crop is sold by the Hops Marketing Board, a less romantic but more efficient system of disposal.

There were usually some bunches of Irish cattle at these fairs and the dealers in charge were pretty colourful characters. I asked one if the heifers he was selling were in calf or barren. 'I will warrant them any way you wish, sir,' was his reply.

Weyhill had specially-built raised rows where the hurdles were pitched for the sheep-pens. The point of raising the pens is to make the sheep look bigger to the buyers standing below them. An old trick this: when I sell cattle or sheep at home, I always arrange for the buyer to approach them up-hill.

I don't myself like buying sheep at auction in their pens for I like to see the sheep I am about to offer for moving around, then I can spot any that are lame or otherwise deficient. If they are crowded into a pen, the buyer is at a disadvantage so that at most fairs and sales sheep are driven through a ring; in fact it is only in the south of England that the custom of selling in pens exists.

Our local sheep-fairs have now been concentrated into four, all held at Wilton near Salisbury. The most important is on the second Thursday in September when some 20,000 sheep are sold. It used to be more than a sheep-fair for I can remember seeing a few workers looking for a change of job; cowmen had a wisp of cow's hair in their lapels, and a carter a plait of whipcord. Now they use the classified pages of the farming and local papers to advertise their wants.

Wilton fair is quite a social occasion, drawing farmers from several counties; it's a chance to compare notes on the harvest which has just ended, and to get an idea of what sheep-prices are likely to reach. I seldom send anything there because the cost of getting stock to market is high and there is also the auctioneer's commission to be paid. Instead I go to see if there are any cheap sheep to buy. There is a great variation in price between the four sales at Wilton. If, at the first sale in August, the price of ewes is low, it will usually increase at the next two, but if it is high, then it will almost certainly drop. The art is to guess whether the first sale is the dearest or the cheapest. If you get that one right, you can make a great deal of money. If not, you can bite the bullet.

I am often tempted to buy some ewes if they look really cheap, as this will enable me to cull a few more of my old ones when I go through the flock with my shepherd in September to decide which are to be kept and which are past their prime. This decision is made on the state of their teeth. A sheep has eight incisor teeth on its lower jaw at birth. These are lamb's teeth. At eighteen months it will produce two permanent broad teeth, at two and a half years, two more, at three and a half years, two more, completing the tally at just over four years old. By which time it will have had three crops of lambs. After that there is no certain way of telling a sheep's age, unless the breeder has earmarked it at the year of birth. After the sheep become full-mouth, their teeth begin to deteriorate and they can lose some. This is controlled by their feed to some extent: if they have been living on soft pasture, their teeth will last a long time, but if they have been gnawing turnips, they can lose them very quickly. As the sheep's well-being depends entirely on the efficiency of its mouth as a mowing-machine, the teeth must be in good order.

My shepherd and I go through the ewes every September to see which ones will be able to stand another year in the Tangley environment of rather hard grazing with a lot of stones. If the teeth have worn down evenly to the gum they will live for several years after the full-mouth stage, but if the mouths 'break', that is lose odd teeth, they can deteriorate very quickly once winter comes. Each ewe is studied and her udder is also tested. It is no good letting her bear a couple of lambs only to find she has no milk to feed them with. However, even if a ewe has no teeth, I will keep her another year if she is strong and in good condition because the more lambs I can get from a ewe, the less depreciation she has to bear, but she will be put in a separate flock for extra feeding. I find in general that I have to renew about a quarter of the flock annually, usually with ewe lambs purchased a year before. For these I travel to Cumbria where every September there are huge sales of store-lambs off the Pennines, as there are in many of the hill areas. These are nearly all first-class hybrids between a hill ewe and a lowland ram. The rams are especially bred for the job and are based on the Border Leicester, a Scottish sheep. This is an enormous animal with a Roman nose, and its chief characteristics are prolificacy and milking ability. Its conformation is poor, producing a lamb which in general is too big for the modern trade, but crossbred with a hill sheep of whatever breed, the progeny will fit extremely well into the lowland lamb-breeding flock. There is a great deal of fashion in these rams. Their excellence appears to be based on their performance in the show ring and at auction.

Critics, usually Southern farmers, accuse the ram-breeders of disregarding hardiness and productive efficiency. They respond by pointing out the very high prices their rams make in the sales; such prices they insist, are a sure guide to the breed's worth, being the result of a consensus of the keenest judges, the buyers. But such prices are seldom what they seem on the surface. Most of the ram sales are between members of the same pedigree-breeding society. There is a good deal of what could be called taking in each other's washing. A breeder may arrange beforehand to give X thousand pounds for a ram on condition the vendor buys one of his, and so on. This goes on in all pedigree circles to some extent. It is not a matter of self-delusion. A good advertisement for a breeding ram is the price its sire is reported to have fetched. This is very much the belief in Scotland but diminishes on the road south. I can claim to be the first farmer to go to Cumberland and to bring back to Hampshire, Mule or Greyfaced lambs from Swaledale ewes sired by Blue-Faced Leicester rams. They are now the predominant crossbred used in the south of England. Thirty years ago I visited Lazonby in Cumberland for the first time and bought several hundred of these crossbreds because they looked cheap. Some I sold to neighbours, the rest I farmed myself. I carried on buying and trading in them and one of my sons has now taken on this part of the business and expanded it.

There are other crosses such as the Border Leicester/Cheviot and there is also a Scottish counterpart to the Swaledale which is known as the Blackface, but for many years now Blackface ram-breeders have been mainly lowland farmers. Blackface rams make very high prices but because of their breeding farms they are no longer really hill sheep, moreover I think that the crossbred lamb out of the Blackface is too short and that the breeders are concentrating on too compact a type.

Buying my lambs is always an interesting exercise. The lambs are always shown in a covered ring in lots of thirty or forty. I like mine to match as well as they can, and as the sale begins I form a mind-picture of the size and shape of the lambs I wish to buy, and of the price I shall pay for them. Then, as they come into the ring I match them with this picture. It does not do to be carried away by the auctioneer. There are probably more than 20,000 of the same type of lamb to be sold in the day, and there are always other lots. Every vendor of breeding-sheep everywhere claims that his sheep come off the highest and poorest land in the kingdom. Alston Moor is the nearest high point to Lazonby and if all vendors told the truth about where their lambs were bred there could hardly have been standing-room there the previous spring. A great many of these crossbreds are born on the lower fields, and sometimes not on the hills at all. I don't listen to the propaganda, I look for scale, for a well-proportioned body which looks to me as though it will develop into a big long sheep on my better country. A long-backed ewe will have a long-backed lamb which will carry more loin and not so much fat and she will have plenty of room for a womb in which to grow two, or even three, lambs.

A feature of the sales is the luck-money handed back by the vendor, something we never have in the South. It works out as a very important discount. When I was busy buying, I used to engage a drover to look after the sheep so that I could collect the luck-money before the owners disappeared.

I usually buy 300 or 400 of these lambs every year and run them on my own uneconomic downland areas or send them to neighbours to keep for the first winter. All I earn off them the first year is about three pounds from the sale of their wool, but the total cost of each ewe lamb bought in Cumberland will be from ten to fifteen pounds cheaper than if I had bought it as a ewe at a local fair such as Wilton the following year. As too early a pregnancy would be a great drain on their system which would show up in after years, I only occasionally run a ram with the biggest of the ewe lambs the first year.

A recent interesting development at a Swaledale ram-sale was to see several Scots bidding actively. They were after rams to improve the Blackface. If this goes on, the Blue Faced Leicester will displace the Border Leicester as the main sire for crossbred ewes and the Mule will become the most popular breed even in the Scottish lowlands. That is of course until the fashion changes.

As you must have gathered by now I am highly sceptical about pedigree-breeders and their stock. This all started a long time ago when a neighbouring landowner had a well-known herd of beef-cattle and his manager bought a very expensive bull. In due course the owner died and there was a dispersal sale. The progeny of that particular bull sold very well indeed, and some time afterwards I met the herdsman, now retired. 'Your bull did you very well,' I remarked. 'He did, but he didn't,' was the reply. 'You see,' he told me, 'the one we bought was infertile but the manager had forgotten to insure him so instead of making a fuss we used a closely-related bull and he did us just as well. The real bull never sired a calf.'

Bulls and rams can be infertile, cows and ewes can be barren, in which case they must be culled. In an average year, ten ewes out of every hundred won't rear lambs: four will die, four will be barren and two for some reason will not rear their lambs. The dead of course are buried. The barreners and non-rearers are sold in the spring when there is often a very good trade for ewe mutton, but my sale of culled ewes cannot match my purchase of young sheep. Even if there is a good trade, their prices don't come to more than half what they have cost to go into the flock. In the autumn prices are a good deal worse. There is a lot of sheep-meat on the market and no one really wants to eat ewe mutton then. The ewes might, after say five lambings, be worth no more than a third of what they cost as young ewes.

It used to be possible to pay for the new entrants to the flock with the sum of the sale of wool and cull-ewes. This no longer holds good. The wool price has not risen appreciably for the past four or five years, nor has that of cull-ewes. Not all mine go to the butcher. Many are sold to farmers in the west of England to run on soft dairy pastures for the winter and early spring, they will do much better there than on my own hard grazing.

Why do I keep sheep at all? For no better reason than that I always have. First a few as a hobby, when the main enterprise was cows, then like Topsy they have just grown. When they became more than I could handle I engaged a shepherd. It seemed best to have a full-time man, because if the job was left to a spare man on the farm it was never properly done. But I need sufficient sheep to keep the shepherd busy, so Brian has to look after at least 1,200 ewes and their 1,800 lambs. These numbers cannot be allowed to feed on just any old pasture, and have to be cared for like a special crop on well-fertilised pastures which means more expense. It is essential to keep labour costs down by producing a high output. The capital investment involved in keeping sheep is considerable. The flock at any moment is worth around £50,000 for ewes alone, which is a lot and does not compare favourably with a hundred sows which would have a total output of approximately the same number of pigs. These would be worth about £10,000 and their output would be at least 50 per cent higher in money terms than that from my sheep. Other factors also have to be taken into account but that is enough to make my point.

Two of my sons have largely discarded sheep as being too capital-intensive:

one has gone in for pigs and one for arable cropping, but then their land-costs are higher than mine are. The real reason I can afford to keep sheep is that my farm stands me in at the price I bought it at long ago when money was cheap to borrow. I have no landlord to push up my rent and no bank manager increasing my overdraft; I'm lucky.

By mid-September I should have sorted out my flock, culled and sold the old ewes and settled in my new lambs. Now I must decide exactly what strains of winter wheat and barley I want to plant in the ensuing year.

There was a time when plant-breeding in Britain was in the hands of a few university professors and an occasional eccentric working on a shoestring. Any new strains they introduced were pirated as soon as they were known to be good and the breeder got little or no advantage from his efforts. Nearly twenty years ago a law guaranteeing plant-breeders royalty rights was passed, and later, EEC membership brought measures that ensured that no seeds passing through the trade could be sold unless they were properly certified and the rights charged. This was a marvellous opportunity for the breeder and big money came into the field in the hopes of big profits.

Before the 'rights' legislation, most new varieties came from the Continent where there had been rights royalties for a long time. The new strains were few in number but usually well tested. There are now a dozen recommended British varieties of winter wheat and about double that number of spring barley. These recommendations are controlled by the National Institute of Agricultural Botany which runs trials all over the country. With all these strains to choose from it is no easy job to decide on those I want to plant in a week or two. It is rather like picking the winner of the Derby the year before it is run from a very sketchy form-book. Complications include a number of varieties which the form-book states are becoming outclassed but which are still doing very well. There are even some which have never been recommended at all like the most widely-grown spring barley, Golden Promise. It's all very unscientific but we farmers are suspicious of the recommended lists because some of the improvements recorded are often more apparent than real. There is great pressure to get new varieties on the market so as to earn more royalties, and so recoup on the initial investment.

I don't worry about the plant-breeders, if I find that a variety does me well, I keep some of the seed, clean it and resow it myself and so do a great many more farmers. We are not supposed to buy and sell seed outside the trade but many of us do. There is nothing to stop farm-to-farm trading in feed-grains, and nothing to stop anyone sowing feed grain.

We are now advised to sow a number of different varieties of wheat or barley or oats each year so that there is less chance of disease wiping out the whole of our harvest. Some strains are more resistant to certain diseases than others; this resistance-factor is determined by inspection and selection at the plant breeders'. They will start up with a million separate plants and gradually cull out those that fail over the next few years. It takes at least twelve years to develop a

131

new strain in sufficient quantity to put it on the market and there are any number of failures. Part of the trouble is that each strain contains genes which can develop weaknesses which have been concealed until then. Resistance to a certain disease is not a fixed factor and is often influenced by the weather of the year in question. Undoubtedly the situation is made worse by the degree of monoculture which is increasingly being practised.

A possible way out is hybridisation. Maize yields have been increased enormously by the use of hybrid seed, the result of crossing two different strains. Hybrid maize has the same quality of vigour, or heterosis, as does a hybrid of the animal species, such as a mule, but equally like a mule, hybrid seeds cannot reproduce themselves, so each planting of a hybrid seed is a one-generation crop, thus each year's supply of seed has to be especially bred by a very intensive form of husbandry. This is expensive but it answers with maize because the seed-rate is very low, about 20 lbs an acre, and production is high, averaging three tonnes.

But wheat for instance requires a seed-rate of about 140 lbs an acre and as its output is unlikely to be more than two tonnes, hybridisation is not yet a commercial proposition. In addition hybrid wheat seed is much harder to produce than maize in the first place. A possible way out of this dilemma will be to culture or clone the cell of a particularly good strain, a method which has been successful with orchids and pineapples and which produces a plant identical in every respect to the parent, but at present this does not seem a practical possibility with cereals.

My final choice of seed is to some extent governed by the past year's experience, although I have to be careful about this because seasons can alter the performance of varieties out of all knowledge; they do not all react in the same way to different climatic factors. For that reason I delay my choice until I can get some idea of how my harvest has just performed, how the separate varieties have yielded in my soil. By September I should know roughly what each field has actually achieved, although I shall have made rough earlier assessments by eye.

After I have chosen the seeds and when I know which fields I want to plant, September's work is to get as much of the land as I can fit for my most profitable grain crop, winter wheat, and to do this as early as possible.

By September too the various sins and omissions of the year's husbandry are coming home to roost. They are almost invariably entirely my own fault. All too often I have failed to take into account what was happening on one part of the farm because I was concentrating too much on another, then when something started to go wrong, I failed to take remedial action quickly enough. One can of course blame the climate, saying it was too wet or too dry but the impact of droughts and floods is overall less damaging than bad farming. I am never satisfied but then what farmer is? 'Could do better,' my school reports used to tell me, well, now I am trying to.

I am ending my farming year on September 28th in traditional fashion: it is the end of the arable cycle and my harvest is over but on a mixed farm the cereal harvest is only part of the whole. My sheep and pigs contribute more to the farm's economy than do the crops and I am harvesting sheep for most of the summer and pigs all the year round every week. Even the grain in store has to be sold and it will take several weeks or months to complete the sales in order to make the best of the market. September is no longer a time for relaxation, for enjoying the fruits of harvest home, it is a period of frenzied activity preparing to sow next year's harvest.

There is no real end or beginning to a farming year. Cropping is decided years in advance, every act of husbandry has to relate to both the cropping that has passed and that which is to come. To maintain my flock of ewes and my herd of pigs in staggered age-groups is a matter of two or three years' advance planning. Even taking on a boy apprentice to begin his life in farming has to be assessed in relation to future labour needs.

In reality farming is best described as a series of twelve-month circles revolving into an endless spiral within which every farmer is a prisoner. His only escape is to die or to retire and few farmers retire willingly in this country.

I most certainly have no intention of so doing. On October 1st, 1982, I shall begin my fiftieth year in farming on my own account and unless frustrated by death or infirmity I certainly don't intend it to be my last. My firm intention is to continue to do the best I can for the farm and my pocket. Even if the performance fails to match the promise, I know I shall enjoy the exercise.

There is no great goal to be worked for in a lifetime's farming. The best I can claim in the way of achievement is that I have kept a few hundred acres of England producing food for half a century and they are doing so better now than they did when I started. My land is in good heart and I have gained experience as I went along and experience is a wonderful asset in farming.

I have had a marvellous life doing exactly what I wanted to do within the disciplines imposed by keeping my farm profitable in all circumstances. You may think I hark a bit too much towards the money side but without profit farming can be very distressing.

The precepts I have tried to live by are quite simple: to farm as if I were going to live for ever, and to live as if I were going to die tomorrow. I have certainly kept the first.

HARVEST 1982 – Cropping

Ashfield Wheat sown October 1981 after spring barley 1981.

Lower Cowdown Wheat sown November 1981 after wheat following grass grazed by sheep.

Cowdown Barley sown March 1982 after barley 1981. This is a difficult field cleared out of woodland twenty-five years ago and still not right yet.

Burrfield Grass sown August 1981 carrying five ewes and their lambs – an acre – a total of fourteen animals.

Little Meadows A permanent pasture made up of three small fields and copses cleared in 1960. Will be put into Burrfield eventually.

Copse Ground Almost pure clay for the most part. *Northern* area sixty acres oats after grass-grazed. There is an acidity problem here and oats tolerate this condition. After the oats are harvested the field will be limed and sown to wheat. *Southern* forty acres first sown October 1981 with winter oats. These failed in frost and the area replanted with spring barley sown late March 1982.

North Field Has been in grass for five years, will be ploughed in summer 1982 for wheat after hay made on it. Wheat for 1983 harvest.

Great Heath Wheat sown October 1981 after barley after wheat after grass. Both this and Ashfield cleaned up from very bad couch problems by spraying the growing crop.

Big Pond Permanent grass for thirty years. Difficult to cultivate, steep and very variable soil.

Clay Copse Cleared out of cut-over woodland in 1955. Sown direct to grass and kept in it owing to stones and tree roots. Could be ploughed if money gets short.

East End and Stoney Heath Barley sown March 1982 after wheat after barley after grass. As name implies very stony and very variable in soil running from chalk to clay.

Pill Heath Common Cleared from common in 1950 and cultivated since. Belongs to Ministry of Agriculture; sown to barley October 1981 following wheat following grass.

Reservoir Barley sown March 1982 replacing barley (sown October 1981) which was eaten out by rooks.

Brickhill Sown to barley 1982 March. Kept in barley because it is difficult to know what to do with it isolated as it is.

Ashfield   originally two fields.
Cowdown Upper and Lower   originally two fields and woodland.
Burrfield   originally five fields.
Copse Ground   originally four fields.
Great Heath   originally two fields.
Clay Copse   originally two fields and woodland – unploughable.
East End   originally five fields and three woods.

Main area seven enclosures – 607 acres 1982 – in 1943 were twenty-five fields and five woods.

The Year's Weather

I wrote this book during the winter of 1981/2 which climatically turned out to be one of the most difficult I can remember. October and November were very wet and sowing was finally completed in December. Then there was a nasty cold spell with zero temperatures over Christmas. There was a thaw around New Year and then, just when things were looking good, there was another cold spell followed by heavy rain, interrupted by a dry spell in March just long enough to get the spring corn in, and then there was a drought from early April until mid-June when I really thought the crops would die. Then it seemed to rain for a month but stopped in time for harvest, having spoilt all my hay.

   In spite of, or perhaps because of all this, the yields overall were very good indeed, quite the best I have enjoyed since I have been at Tangley. I can only hope the next twelve months will be as good.

HARVEST 1982 – Yield

Ashfield	2.24 tonnes an acre, the worst wheat yield probably due to drought in early summer.
Lower Cowdown	Wheat. 2.63 tonnes an acre.
Upper Cowdown	Spring barley. 2.11 tonnes an acre sold for malting.
Copse ground	
Northern area	Oats. 2.66 tonnes per acre.
Great Heath	Wheat. 2.73 tonnes per acre.
East End	Spring barley. 1.77 tonnes per acre.
Pill Heath Common	Winter barley suffered deer and rabbit damage. 1.78 tonnes an acre
Reservoir	Spring barley. 1.96 tonnes an acre.
Brickhill	Spring barley. 1.95 tonnes an acre.

In addition I harvested a further 100 acres of wheat and barley on land I rent and grazed a further 90 acres of pasture.

Total overall harvest was 1,370 tonnes of grain.

1,870 lambs were sold.

1,500 of them fat.

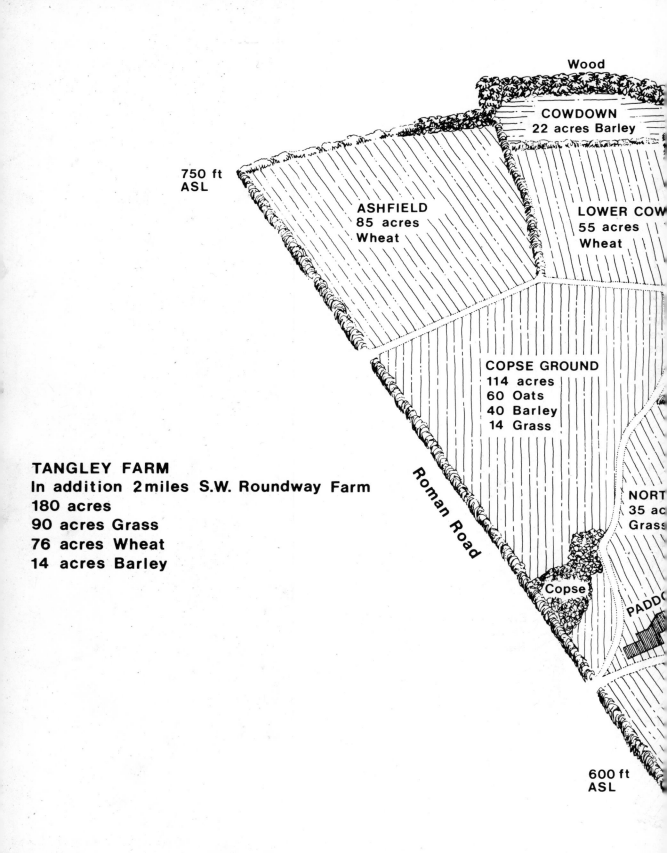

Wood

COWDOWN
22 acres Barley

750 ft
ASL

ASHFIELD
85 acres
Wheat

LOWER COW
55 acres
Wheat

COPSE GROUND
114 acres
60 Oats
40 Barley
14 Grass

Roman Road

TANGLEY FARM
In addition 2 miles S.W. Roundway Farm
180 acres
90 acres Grass
76 acres Wheat
14 acres Barley

NORT
35 ac
Grass

Copse

PADDO

600 ft
ASL